# INTRODUCTION

Congratulations! You are taking a huge step to transforming your immune system and your entire life by investing your time and effort to learn more and more about my "nutritarian" eating style. This workbook works side-by-side with the Super Immunity book, transforming your learning from passive reading to active participation. No matter what your initial reason for purchasing this program, by now you know you have an opportunity to supercharge your immune system to protect you against the common cold, other infections and even cancers. As a bonus side effect, following a nutritarian approach also protects against diabetes and heart disease, meaning that you can live longer and live in excellent health.

I have designed this workbook to help clarify and reinforce the key concepts that are present-ed in my Super Immunity book. Some repetition is intentional to make sure you understand how to apply the most important concepts.

Most importantly, use this booklet as a workbook, to write in, highlight and rein-force the concepts you learned from reading the book and watching the videos. Fill in your personal information and track your progress. A calendar section is provided so that you can check off your diet and exercise goals each day. Let me know how you do, of course I want to hear about your success, but I also want to help you overcome any obstacle that may interfere with you achieving your goals. Hopefully the informational tools you have purchased and are studying plus the extra support available at DrFuhrman.com will make sure you reach your goals.

## HERE'S TO YOUR ACHIEVING SUPER IMMUNITY!

# Review of Core Concepts

## H = N/C

Your future Health (H) will increase as your Nutrient (N)* to Calorie (C) ratio increases
*Nutrient (N) refers to micronutrients*

The secret to a long life and effective disease protection is to eat a diet lower in calories but higher in nutrients. It is all about nutrient bang per caloric buck. This is illustrated by my health equation. Your health expectancy is predicted by your nutrient intake divided by your intake of calories or H = N / C.

This simple mathematical formula is the basis of nutritional science and nutritional healing. For you to be in excellent health your diet must be nutrient-rich (micronutrients) and you must not overeat on calories (macronutrients). The uniqueness of my approach centers on the concept that micronutrient adequacy also suppresses the desire to overeat.

The nutrient density in your body's tissues is proportional to the nutrient density of your diet. When your body's cells have adequate micronutrient density, the body's ability to self-repair and resist disease is heightened.

An important consideration in understanding this formula has to do with micronutrient diversity, not just the absolute number of micronutrients. Micronutrient adequacy means we achieve enough of all beneficial nutrients, not merely higher amounts of a select few, while other micronutrient needs go unfulfilled. Consider mushrooms to illustrate this concept of micronutrient diversity. Mushrooms may not contain very high amounts of vitamins and minerals, but they contain a significant amount of protective phytochemicals not found in other foods, such as aromatase inhibitors and angiogenesis inhibitors. Even a small amount of mushrooms in the diet adds more micronutrient diversity, even though they are not the highest scoring food when we add up all their micronutrients.

So focus on the nutritional quality of what you eat, but also on the proper spectrum of foods that supply the full symphonic orchestra of human requirements. This means that certain foods such as onions, seeds, mushrooms, berries, beans and tomatoes aid in achieving micronutrient quality and contribute to the numerator of the above equation, even though they are not at the top of my food scoring system.

The key of this high-nutrient approach is this: You achieve superior health, a properly functioning immune system, and permanent weight control by eating more nutrient-rich foods and fewer high-calorie, low-nutrient foods. It works because the more high-nutrient food you consume, the less low-nutrient food you desire. Since the desire for these unhealthful foods will naturally diminish, what you need to do is focus on learning how to enjoy eating more high-nutrient food.

## What is Super Immunity?

Super Immunity can best be defined as the body's immune system working to its fullest potential. With Super Immunity, you will hardly ever get sick, and on the rare occasions when you do, you will bounce back quickly. Plus, when your immune system is working to its fullest potential, you are building powerful defenses against cancer. The transition from average immunity to Super Immunity is a crucial component of excellent health, and it can save your life.

## Why do we need Super Immunity?

American adults catch on average two to four colds per year, and children catch six to ten. Mild viral infections, in someone without a well-functioning immune system, can linger on for weeks and even develop serious complications. We also need Super Immunity because we are now exposed to more dangerous infections from around the world than ever before. Infectious diseases are quickly globalized by travel and trade, and the development of antibiotic resistance poses a major risk to human health. Importantly, the same immune cells that protect us against infectious diseases also protect us against cancer. One in four deaths in the U.S. is due to cancer, and deaths from infectious diseases have doubled since 1980—we need Super Immunity now more than ever.[1,2]

## The American diet suppresses immune function and promotes chronic disease.

The typical American diet gets over 60 percent of its calories from processed foods (primarily composed of white flour products, sweeteners, and oils), 25.5 percent from animal products, and only 10 percent from unrefined plant foods—and about half of that 10 percent is white potato products, mostly fries and chips! So all in all, only about 5 percent of calories in the American diet come from foods that contain a significant amount of protective phytochemicals.[3] The American diet is grossly deficient in hundreds of these important plant-derived, immunity-building compounds. Consuming calories without the presence of antioxidants, vitamins, and other phytochemicals leads to a build-up of waste products in our cells. So when you eat white bread or other processed foods, the body can't remove normal cellular wastes that build up without the presence of a significant level of plant-derived antioxidant and phytochemical nutrients. When our cells don't have the raw materials needed for normal function it ages us prematurely and causes disease.

## American Diet by Calories

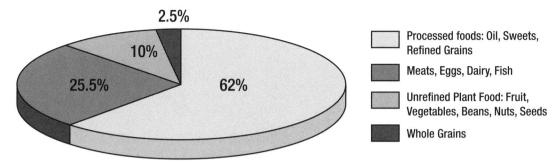

Legend:
- Processed foods: Oil, Sweets, Refined Grains
- Meats, Eggs, Dairy, Fish
- Unrefined Plant Food: Fruit, Vegetables, Beans, Nuts, Seeds
- Whole Grains

### The secret to Super Immunity is superior nutrition.

A healthy body with a high functioning immune system is resistant to viral attack. Our vulnerability to a virus and our inability to fight off the virus once exposed are directly affected by the quality of our everyday diet.

The foods highest in life-extending micronutrients and lowest in calories (high N/C ratio) are green vegetables. They form the basis of my nutritarian diet. The key component to reach excellent health and Super Immunity is to eat more greens, beans, onions, mushrooms, berries, and seeds. As you eat larger amounts of these protective foods you will meet your body's micronutrient needs and naturally reduce the amount of animal products and processed foods in your diet without gimmicks, calorie counting, or portion control.

The human body has amazing protective and healing powers, but only if we give it the right raw materials to work with. What if we could build immune defenses with superior nutrition to develop Super Immunity – defenses so strong that more than 90 percent of cancers would not occur? What if these same nutritional practices enabled us to age more slowly and maintain excellent health into our later years? Food gives us more than just energy – modern nutritional science has uncovered powerful effects of phytochemicals in certain plant foods that strengthen immune function and protect us from cancer. This workbook and accompanying materials will help you understand this new science and put it into action. It's not just about getting through flu season – it's about living with excellent health for the rest of your life.

### How do phytochemicals contribute to immune function?

Phytochemicals are plant-derived chemical compounds important for growth and survival of the plant – more than just vitamins and minerals, but a vast array of tens of thousands of plant-produced nutrients. They came about for the benefit of the plant world, but the human immune system evolved depending on these phytochemicals for its optimal functioning.

**Phytochemicals**

- Induce detoxification enzymes
- Control oxidative stress (antioxidants)
- Detoxify carcinogens
- Protect cell structures from damage by toxins
- Fuel DNA repair mechanisms
- Impede replication of cells with damaged DNA
- Have antifungal, antibacterial, antiviral effects
- Improve immune cells' cytotoxic power

Phytochemicals from many plant foods work synergistically together to fuel the self-healing and protective properties of the human body.

# Super Foods for Super Immunity: G-BOMBS

## G – Greens

Raw leafy greens contain less than 100 calories per pound, and are packed with nutrients. Leafy greens contain substances that protect blood vessels, and are associated with reduced risk of diabetes.[4] Greens are an excellent tool for weight loss, since they can be consumed in virtually unlimited quantities. Leafy greens are also the most nutrient-dense of all foods, but unfortunately are only consumed in miniscule amounts in a typical American diet. We should follow the example of our closest living relatives—chimpanzees and gorillas—who consume tens of pounds of green leaves every day.

The majority of calories in green vegetables, including leafy greens, come from protein, and this plant protein is packaged with beneficial phytochemicals: Green vegetables are rich in folate (the natural form of folic acid) and calcium, and contain small amounts of omega-3 fatty acids. Leafy greens are also rich in antioxidant pigments called carotenoids, specifically lutein and zeaxanthin, which are the carotenoids known to promote healthy vision.[5]

Several leafy greens and other green vegetables belong to the cruciferous family of vegetables.

| CRUCIFEROUS VEGETABLES | | |
|---|---|---|
| Arugula | Cauliflower | Red cabbage |
| Bok choy | Collards | Rutabaga |
| Broccoli | Horseradish | Turnips |
| Broccoli rabe | Kale | Turnip greens |
| Broccolini | Kohlrabi | Watercress |
| Brussels sprouts | Mustard greens | |
| Cabbage | Radish | |

All vegetables contain protective micronutrients and phytochemicals, but cruciferous vegetables have a unique chemical composition—they contain glucosinolates, and when their cell walls are broken by blending, chopping, or chewing, a chemical reaction converts glucosinolates to isothiocyanates (ITCs)—compounds with a variety of potent anti-cancer effects. In addition, some ITCs have been shown specifically to enhance immune function or inhibit infection. Also, ITCs and antioxidants activate a transcription factor called Nrf-2, which activates gene expression to produce detoxification enzymes, a natural defense system in our cells.

### Cancer-preventive actions of ITCs: [6]

- Angiogenesis inhibition
- Antioxidant effects
- Anti-inflammatory effects
- Detoxify carcinogens
- Prevent carcinogen-DNA binding
- Promote repair of damaged DNA
- Promote death of cancerous cells
- Promote excretion of estrogens

### Immune-supporting, antiviral and antibacterial properties of ITCs:

- Indole-3 carbinol (I3C) and diindolylmethane (DIM) enhance interferon responsiveness, enabling efficient attack of microbial invaders.[7]

- DIM resolves cervical dysplasia and is being studied as a treatment for other viral infections.[8]

- ITCs increase resistance against infection by drug-resistant bacteria.[9]

- ITCs inhibit growth of *H. Pylori* (a bacteria associated with ulcers and increased risk of stomach cancer).[10]

- There is also evidence that cruciferous phytochemicals help to maintain adequate numbers of certain immune cells in the intestine.[11]

### How to maximize the benefits of cruciferous vegetables

In order for us to get the maximum benefit, these vegetables must be cut, chopped, or crushed to break up cell walls and initiate the chemical reaction that forms ITCs. The more you chop before cooking (or chew if you are eating raw) the better. Some ITC benefit may be lost with boiling or steaming, so we get the maximum benefit from eating cruciferous vegetables raw – however some production of ITC in cooked cruciferous vegetables may occur in the gut once the vegetables have been ingested. Consuming a large variety of these ITC-rich cruciferous vegetables within an overall nutrient-dense diet can provide us with a profound level of protection against cancer.

## B – Beans

Beans (and other legumes as well) are a power-house of superior nutrition, and the most nutrient-dense carbohydrate source. They act as an anti-diabetes and weight-loss food because they are digested slowly, having a stabilizing effect on blood sugar, which promotes satiety and helps to prevent food cravings. Plus they contain soluble fiber, which lowers cholesterol levels.[12] Beans are unique foods because of their very high levels of fiber and resistant starch, carbohydrates that are not broken down by digestive enzymes. Fiber and resistant starch not only reduce total the number of calories absorbed from beans, but are also fermented by intestinal bacteria into fatty acids that help to prevent colon cancer.[13] Eating beans, peas, or lentils at least twice a week has been found to decrease colon cancer risk by 50 percent.[14] Legume intake also provides significant protection against oral, larynx, pharynx, stomach, and kidney cancers.[15]

| Glycemic Load, Resistant Starch and Fiber in Common Carbohydrate Foods [16] | | | | | |
|---|---|---|---|---|---|
| FOOD | GL | % RS | % FIBER | % RS + FIBER | DR. FUHRMAN'S ANDI SCORE |
| Black beans | 6 | 26.9 | 42.6 | 69.5 | 61 |
| Northern beans | 6 | 28.0 | 41.1 | 69.1 | 77 |
| Red kidney beans | 8 | 24.6 | 36.8 | 61.4 | 64 |
| Lentils | 9 | 25.4 | 33.1 | 58.5 | 72 |
| Split peas | 6 | 24.5 | 33.1 | 57.6 | 43 |
| Corn | 18 | 25.2 | 19.6 | 44.7 | 45 |
| Barley | 16 | 18.2 | 17.0 | 35.2 | 25 |
| Millet | 25 | 12.6 | 5.4 | 18.0 | 23 |
| Rolled oats | 13 | 7.2 | 10.0 | 17.2 | 36 |
| Black/wild rice | 14 | (unknown) | 5.0 | - | 27 |
| White rice | 26 | 14.1 | 1.5 | 15.6 | 13 |
| Whole wheat | 11 | 1.7 | 12.1 | 13.8 | 33 |
| White pasta | 21 | 3.3 | 5.6 | 8.9 | 16 |
| Butternut squash | 8 | (unknown) | 2.0 | - | 241 |
| Sweet potato | 14 | (unknown) | 3.0 | - | 181 |
| White potato | 29 | 7.0 | 2.0 | 9.0 | 27 |

*(1-cup portion or 1 medium baked white or sweet potato)*

If you add up the percent of resistant starch (RS) (mostly unabsorbed) and the fiber (which also is not absorbed), and make comparisons, you will see why beans are the preferred starch source. The % RS + fiber is handy measurement to illustrate the favorable glycemic and weight-maintaining effects of beans compared to other high carbohydrate foods.

## O – Onions

Onions, along with leeks, garlic, shallots, and scallions, make up the Allium family of vegetables, which have beneficial effects on the cardiovascular and immune systems, as well as anti-diabetic and anti-cancer effects. Allium vegetables are known for their characteristic organosulfur compounds. Similar to the ITCs in cruciferous vegetables, organosulfur compounds are released when onions are chopped, crushed, or chewed. These compounds prevent the development of cancers by detoxifying carcinogens, halting cancer cell growth, and blocking angiogenesis.[17] One large European study found striking risk reductions in the participants who consumed the greatest quantities of onions or garlic for oral, esophageal, colorectal, laryngeal, breast, ovarian, and prostate cancers. A 55-80 percent reduction of almost all major cancers.[18] Amazing! Onions also contain high concentrations of health-promoting flavonoid antioxidants, predominantly quercetin, and red onions also contain at least 25 different anthocyanins.[19] Quercetin slows tumor development, suppresses growth and proliferation and induces cell death in colon cancer cells.[20] Flavonoids also have anti-inflammatory effects that may contribute to cancer prevention.[21]

**Onions: how to maximize anti-cancer activity and minimize eye irritation**

The secret is to make sure that the onion is cold before you cut it, because more of the sulfur compounds will be released into the air if it is at room temperature. Even putting the onion in the freezer for 5 minutes is sufficient. You can also use a fan to blow the gaseous compounds away from you if you like. The root is the part of the onion with the most biological activity—we want those sulfur compounds in our dish, so we want to use as much of the root as we can.

**The best way to cut an onion:**

1. Place the onion down with the root facing away from you

2. Cut the end of the root off, preserving as much root as possible

3. Cut off the other end, then cut a slit in the side and remove the outer skin

4. Make sure to then cut or chop the onion finely, slice thinly, or put it in a food processor before adding to your soup or vegetable dish to maximize the production of sulfur compounds.

## M – Mushrooms

Mushroom phytochemicals are thought to inhibit tumor growth and viral infection by stimulating the immune system.[22] Commonly eaten mushrooms (white, cremini, and portobello) also contain a special protein that can recognize many cancer cells and then activates the body's defenses.[23] Mushroom phytochemicals may even be helpful for autoimmune diseases because of their anti-inflammatory and immune-modulating effects.[24]

Consuming mushrooms regularly is associated with decreased risk of breast, stomach, and colorectal cancers.[25] In one recent Chinese study, women who ate at least 10 grams of fresh mushrooms each day (about one mushroom per day) had a 64% decreased risk of breast cancer. Even more dramatic protection was gained by women who ate 10 grams of mushrooms and drank green tea daily – an 89% decrease in risk for premenopausal women, and 82% for postmenopausal women.[26] All types of edible mushrooms all have anti-cancer properties—some are anti-inflammatory, stimulate the immune system, prevent DNA damage, slow cancer cell growth, cause programmed cancer cell death, and inhibit angiogenesis.[27] In addition to these properties, mushrooms are unique because they contain aromatase inhibitors—compounds that can block the production of estrogen. These compounds are thought to be largely responsible for the preventive effects of mushrooms against breast cancer—in fact, there are aromatase-inhibiting drugs on the market that are used to treat breast cancer. Regular consumption of dietary aromatase inhibitors is an excellent strategy for prevention, and it turns out that even the most commonly eaten mushrooms (white, cremini, and portobello) have a high anti-aromatase activity.

| LEVEL OF ANTI-AROMATASE ACTIVITY | MUSHROOMS |
| --- | --- |
| HIGH | White button, white stuffing, cremini, portobello, reishi, maitake |
| MEDIUM | Shiitake, chanterelle, baby button |
| LOW | Oyster, wood ear |

## B – Berries (and Pomegranates)

Blueberries, strawberries, blackberries, and pomegranates are true super foods. Naturally sweet and juicy, berries are low in sugar and high in nutrients—they are among the best foods you can eat. Their vibrant colors mean that they are full of antioxidants, including flavonoids and antioxidant vitamins. The juice and seeds of the pomegranate have antioxidant, anti-cancer, and anti-inflammatory properties. Pomegranates, like mushrooms, have anti-aromatase activity, so they are especially protective against breast cancer. Pomegranate antioxidants are also protective against heart disease—pomegranate naturally lowers blood pressure, and has even been shown to reduce atherosclerotic plaque in humans.[28] Berries, like pomegranate, are some of the highest antioxidant foods in existence. Berries' plentiful antioxidant content confers both cardioprotective and anti-cancer effects, such as reducing blood pressure, reducing inflammation, preventing DNA damage, inhibiting tumor angiogenesis, and stimulating the body's own antioxidant enzymes.[29] Berry consumption has been linked to reduced risk of diabetes, cancers and cognitive decline.[30] Berries are an excellent food for the brain—berry consumption improves both motor coordination and memory.[31]

## S – Seeds

Nuts and seeds contain healthy fats and are rich in a spectrum of micronutrients including phytosterols, minerals, and antioxidants. They are not only tasty and healthy, but portable too—nuts and seeds are great to take along while traveling. Countless studies have demonstrated the cardiovascular benefits of nuts, and including nuts in the diet aids in weight maintenance and diabetes prevention.[32] The nutritional profiles of seeds are similar to nuts when it comes to healthy fats, minerals, and antioxidants, but seeds are also abundant in trace minerals, higher in protein than nuts, and each kind of seed is nutritionally unique. Flax, chia, and hemp seeds and walnuts are extremely rich sources of omega-3 fats (remember that flaxseeds must be ground to get the omega-3 benefit). In addition to the omega-3s, flaxseeds are rich in fiber and lignans. Flaxseed consumption protects against heart disease by a number of different mechanisms, and lignans, which are abundant in both flaxseeds and sesame seeds, have anti-cancer effects.[33] Sunflower seeds are especially rich in protein and minerals. Pumpkin seeds are rich in iron and calcium and are a good source of zinc. Sesame seeds have the greatest amount of calcium of any food in the world, and provide abundant amounts of vitamin E, which is important for the immune system. Also, black sesame seeds are extremely rich in antioxidants.[34] The healthy fats in seeds and nuts also aid in the absorption of nutrients when eaten with vegetables.

# SUPER FOODS FOR SUPER IMMUNITY: ANTI-ANGIOGENIC FOODS

Angiogenesis is a complex physiological process by which new blood vessels are formed from previously existing ones—this process is rare in healthy adults. In cancer, angiogenesis is initiated when a tumor becomes large enough to need its own blood supply in order to fuel further growth. The tumor sends signals to nearby blood vessels to branch off and supply it with oxygen and nutrients, and these new vessels allow a small non-threatening microscopic tumor to grow and become invasive and dangerous. Since angiogenesis is rare in healthy adults and necessary for tumor growth, several anti-angiogenic drugs have been developed as cancer therapies. Angiogenesis also plays a role in obesity—as fat tissue grows it sends angiogenic signals to nearby blood vessels.

Many plant foods contain natural angiogenesis inhibitors. If our diet contains plenty of these mild angiogenesis inhibitors, theoretically we can suppress the expansion of fat tissue and prevent tumor progression.

| ANTI-ANGIOGENIC FOODS & NUTRIENTS[35] | | |
|---|---|---|
| Mushrooms: maitake, enoki, reishi | Black rice | Cinnamon |
| Grapes | Turmeric | Ginger |
| Citrus fruits | Berries | Peppers |
| Cocoa | Cruciferous vegetables | Tea (black and green) |
| Soybeans | Allium vegetables (the onion family) | Vitamin E |
| Flaxseed | Spinach | Omega-3 fatty acids |
| Pomegranate | Tomato | |

Also remember that some of the staple foods of the standard American diet promote angiogenesis—white flour products, oils, and high-cholesterol foods.[36]

# DR. FUHRMAN'S NUTRITARIAN FOOD PLATE©

Avoid: Factory-farmed animal products, especially Red Meat, Cheese, Sweets, Processed Foods, White Rice & White Flour

Limit: (Less than 10%) Naturally raised and wild animal products, Poultry, Eggs, Fish, Dairy, Oil, and White Potato

## Vegetables
1/2 Raw and 1/2 Cooked
30-60% of calories

e.g. collard/mustard/turnip greens, kale, swiss chard spinach, Brussels sprouts, bok choy, cabbage, broccoli, asparagus, squash, carrots, peppers, onions, garlic, tomatoes, zucchini, mushrooms, lettuce

## Beans
10-40% of calories
e.g. kidney, cannellini, pinto, black, chickpeas, lentils, split peas, black-eyed peas, soybeans

## Whole Grains
20% or less of calories
e.g. black rice, brown rice, oats, whole wheat, quinoa

## Seeds/Nuts
10-40% of calories
e.g. chia, hemp, flax, sesame, pumpkin, sunflower, pine nuts, walnuts, almonds, pistachios, cashews

## Fruits
10-40% of calories
e.g. berries, cherries, pomegranates, oranges, melons, kiwi, pineapples, peaches, plums, pears, grapes, bananas

## 5 Simple Rules for a Powerful Immune System

1. Eat a large salad every day.

2. Eat at least a half-cup serving of beans or lentils each day in a soup or stew, on top of a salad, or in another dish.

3. Eat at least three fresh fruits each day, especially berries, pomegranate, cherries, plums, and oranges.

4. Eat at least one ounce of raw nuts and seeds each day, focusing on high omega-3 nuts and seeds (walnuts, hemp, flax, chia).

5. Eat at least one double-size serving of green vegetables daily, either raw, steamed, or cooked into a soup or stew.

## Avoid the 5 Deadliest Foods:

1. Barbequed meat, processed meat, and commercial red meat

2. Fried foods

3. Full-fat dairy products (cheese, ice cream, butter, whole milk) and trans fats (margarine)

4. Soft drinks, sugar, and artificial sweeteners

5. White flour products

# HIGH-NUTRIENT (NUTRITARIAN) EATING: GENERAL GUIDELINES

This immune-protective eating style is designed to emphasize and mix the most powerfully protective foods in the human diet: G-BOMBS—greens, beans, onions, mushrooms, berries, and seeds. Following this eating style means that ninety percent of your daily calories will come from nutrient-rich, whole plant foods.

## Unlimited Foods: G-BOMBS

**Greens, onions, mushrooms and other vegetables:**

This is a vegetable-based diet. Eat as many vegetables as you can. Every lunch and every dinner should begin with a salad or some raw vegetables, and you can eat as many non-starchy vegetables as you desire. Eggplant and beans, mushrooms and beans, greens and beans are all high-nutrient, high-fiber, low-calorie, main dishes. Try them all—and learn various and delicious ways to flavor them.

Occasionally, instead of a salad you can substitute a glass of fresh squeezed raw vegetable juice. Try juicing a combination of carrots and apples, or carrots and cucumbers, or tomatoes and beets. It would also be great to add some greens to the juice.

| High Cruciferous Juice | *Serves 2* |
|---|---|
| 3 medium carrots | |
| 3 cauliflower florets | |
| 1 apple, cored and cut in fourths | |
| 1/2 bunch kale | |
| 2/3 cup watercress with stems | |
| 2 cups broccoli with stems | |

In fact, another great healthy dish is a blended salad—raw greens and fruit blended up into a smooth, delicious drink. Nothing beats a blended salad for getting all those phytonutrients that are potentially damaged with cooking. Raw greens are wonder foods for our health and when you place them in a blender and make a great tasting green smoothie you get powerful nutrient delivery.

Eat a huge portion of cooked green or cruciferous vegetables with dinner—some examples are broccoli, kale, string beans, artichokes, Brussels sprouts, spinach, Swiss chard, cabbage, asparagus, collards, okra, and zucchini. These can be flavored with stewed tomatoes, garlic, onions, mushrooms and other spices.

Make sure to include cruciferous vegetables daily—at least one of your vegetable servings each day should be cruciferous. Onions, garlic, leeks, scallions, shallots, and chives add flavor and anti-cancer compounds with negligible calories. Mushrooms add a chewy, meaty texture to soups, stews, and vegetable dishes. Mushrooms should always be eaten cooked, because they contain a small amount of toxins that dissipate when they are heated. There is a huge variety of mushrooms, and each one will lend a slightly different flavor to your dishes: try button, cremini, portobello, trumpet, shiitake, morel, porcini, maitake, and more.

### Beans: the ideal carbohydrate source

When it comes to choosing your primary carbohydrate source, choose beans over grains. Beans are far superior to whole grains when it comes to nutrient density, and have much smaller glycemic effects because of their resistant starch content. Eat at least one ½ cup serving of beans or lentils each day, either on your salad or in a soup or stew.

### Berries and other fruits

Eat as many fresh fruits as you want, at least three fresh fruits daily. Emphasize berries and pomegranate – these are the highest in nutrient to calorie ratio and have documented anti-cancer effects. Minimize or avoid fruit juice because the presence of the full fiber available in whole fruits slows the absorption of sugars and will suppress appetite. If you like juice, it is better to juice vegetables or add green vegetable to the sweeter carrot, beet or fruit juices to make it less sweet and more nutrient-rich.

### Foods to limit or avoid
- White potatoes
- White flour products, refined grains
- Sugars and processed foods
- Animal products
- Oils
- Salt

### Why limit or avoid white potatoes?

Data from the Nurses' Health Study has implied that white potato consumption is linked to diabetes risk, and furthermore that white potato consumption is more strongly linked to diabetes risk in obese individuals. The researchers made the conclusion that the increased glycemic load (GL) of the women's diets caused by high potato consumption was the major driving force for the increased diabetes risk – not the added fats consumed with the potatoes. To prevent diabetes, it is important for overweight individuals to focus on low glycemic carbohydrate sources, since the data suggests that excess weight makes us more susceptible to the harmful effects of high GL foods.[37] Obesity contributes to insulin resistance, amplifying the hyperglycemia and hyperinsulinemia brought on by high GL foods.

There is evidence that elevated glucose and insulin levels contribute to the development of cancer. Foods with a high GL produce dangerous spikes in blood glucose, consequently resulting in hyperinsulinemia – these include white bread, sugar, and white potatoes. Insulin in high concentrations can initiate growth-promoting actions in cancer cells, both on its own and by raising circulating levels of a growth-promoting hormone called insulin-like growth factor 1 (IGF-1).[38] So it is especially important for those who currently have or have had cancer to focus on low glycemic sources of carbohydrate.

### Why avoid refined grains, sugars, and processed foods?

Avoid all refined carbohydrates such as white bread, pasta, white rice, and sugars – these are high-calorie, high GL foods – they rapidly elevate blood glucose while providing almost no micronutrient value. As mentioned above, there is evidence that elevated glucose and insulin levels contribute to the development of cancer, supporting the possibility that chronic exposure to high-glycemic refined carbohydrates may act directly to promote carcinogenesis. In addition, diets containing large quantities of high GL foods are associated with the risk of diabetes, heart disease, multiple cancers, and overall chronic disease.[39] Most processed foods are primarily a combination of refined grains, sugar, oil, and salt.

### Why limit or avoid animal products?

Animal products are calorie-rich and nutrient-poor foods. For most people in good health, one or two servings of animal products per week would unlikely be damaging to long-term health. However, for those with autoimmune conditions or cancer, even a small amount may be problematic.

Several studies have shown that a vegetarian diet can improve the symptoms of autoimmune diseases. A "leaky gut" is common in those who suffer from autoimmune diseases—this allows incompletely digested food to cross the intestinal wall.[40] Remember that food is our major contact with the external environment. Partially digested animal proteins can bridge the walls of the digestive tract and be absorbed into the circulation. These protein fragments can promote an excessive antibody response that contributes to autoimmune diseases and their symptoms—accordingly, vegetarian diets have been shown in several medical studies to improve autoimmune symptoms.[41]

Dietary protein, especially animal protein, is the major determinant of circulating levels of the growth-promoting hormone IGF-1.[42] IGF-1 is known to contribute to cancer cell proliferation, and elevated circulating IGF-1 is associated with increased risk of several cancers.[43] To minimize the growth signals transmitted to cancerous cells, animal protein should be avoided in individuals who have or have had cancer.

Consumption of red and processed meats is associated with several cancers, and has been deemed a convincing cause of colorectal cancers. Red and processed meats contain a number of potentially carcinogenic substances: N-nitroso compounds are especially high in processed meats due to added preservatives; cooking red meats at high temperatures forms additional carcinogens called heterocyclic amines and dioxins.[44]

### Why limit or avoid salt?

Sodium is an important mineral that is essential to the body's proper function – however, adding salt (sodium chloride) to food provides us with dangerously high amounts of sodium. High sodium intake is associated with cardiovascular disease, stomach cancer, and osteoporosis.[45] The human body was designed to obtain the sodium it needs from natural foods. Ideally, we should consume less than 1000 mg of sodium each day. Whole plant foods contain less than 50 mg of sodium per 100 calories. Since most of the salt in the Western diet comes from processed and restaurant foods, avoiding salt is easily achieved by focusing on whole, natural plant foods. If you are eating any packaged food, you must read the labels and aim for no more than 300-400 mg of added sodium per day (depending on your size and caloric intake). A good rule of thumb is to choose foods that have less sodium (in mg) than the number of calories per serving. A huge misconception is that "natural" salts, like sea salt, are "healthy" alternatives to table salt. However, these salts are still more than 98% sodium chloride. The trace mineral content is negligible and these salts provide no significant beneficial effect on human health.

### Why avoid oils?

Oils contribute not only to weight gain but also to the high omega-6/omega-3 ratio that is characteristic of the standard American diet. Modern diets, rich in animal products, cooking oils, and margarines supply too much omega-6 fat and not enough omega-3 fat. Both types of fat are essential – the body needs both to properly regulate the inflammatory response.

However, excess omega-6 can result in a shift in the balance toward production of pro-inflammatory substances in the body.

When these fatty acids are ingested in the form of extracted oils, they are rapidly and efficiently absorbed by the body and immediately converted into body fat. If these fatty acids were instead ingested from whole foods, such as nuts and seeds, their absorption would be much slower, over hours, not minutes and they would stimulate fatty acid oxidation, meaning most of them would be burned for our energy needs and not stored. Also the fibers, sterols and stanols in the seeds and nuts would bind some of the fat in the digestive tract, like a sponge,

limiting the bioavailability of the fat. Since we get exposed to less fat calories in nuts and seeds and burn them off (if we remain at a favorable weight) we don't easily retain excess omega-6 fat from nuts and seeds, like we do with oil.

Accordingly, excess omega-6 consumption occurs largely from the oils we add to our foods and this is thought to contribute to several chronic diseases by fueling chronic inflammation.[46] Since omega-3 fat has anti-inflammatory effects and is generally harder to obtain, it is important to focus on consuming sufficient omega-3 and limiting omega-6. Eating plenty of greens and omega-3 rich seeds and nuts (hemp, chia, flax, and walnuts), taking a DHA supplement, and minimizing oils and animal products helps to balance our omega-3 and omega-6 fats.

## Tips for switching to a nutritarian eating style

1. Eat a large, raw salad at least once a day. Put a big sign on your refrigerator that says, "The Salad is the Main Dish."

2. To get additional raw vegetables into your daily diet, add tomatoes, shredded carrots, cabbage, beets, snow peas, or raw broccoli to your salads or enjoy some cut raw vegetables with a nut, seed, or bean-based dip at the beginning of your lunch or dinner.

3. Frozen vegetables are convenient and very nutrient dense. They are picked and then steamed briefly and frozen the same day, locking in the nutrients. Throw a box of frozen artichoke hearts, asparagus, or peas on your salad if you'd like.

4. Consume a large portion of cooked green vegetables. Vegetables such as asparagus, artichokes, kale, collards, broccoli, Brussels sprouts, green beans, baby bok choy, and other greens should be eaten every day. You can also do this by adding these greens to a soup or stew.

5. Always eat mushrooms cooked, not raw. Mushrooms contain mild toxins that dissipate with heat.

6. Reduce animal products: Many people believe that they need animal products to feel good and perform well. Usually, this is the result of a diet change followed by temporary withdrawal symptoms (such as fatigue). People assume that there is a lack

of protein in their new diet, and return to their old diet. Protein deficiency does not cause long-term fatigue. Reducing animal products in your diet may cause temporary fatigue, headaches, and digestive discomfort, but this is just part of the normal detoxification process that most people have to get through when they improve their diet. Start by not eating more than one serving of animal products a day, and limiting the size of the portion to less than four ounces (no larger than the size of a deck of cards). Then, try having only one small serving of animal products every other day. In other words, whether you have two eggs, chicken in your salad or soup, or a turkey sandwich on whole grain pita, make the next day a strict vegetarian day. As you move forward, move up to the next level of superior nutrition by reducing animal products progressively further. Completely avoid fast-food, processed, barbequed or salted meats.

7. Reduce salt intake: It's important to note that high salt intake deadens your taste buds to the subtle delicious flavors found in natural foods. So when you first reduce your salt intake, expect that some of the recipes may taste bland to you. Fortunately, your taste buds adjust to taking in less sodium by becoming more sensitive, so that natural foods will increase in flavor. Your ability to taste, not just sodium more intensely, but also the subtle deliciousness of natural foods increases. This happens over time and it takes about 6-12 weeks on a low salt diet (less than 1000 mg/day) for this change to occur. Do not cook with salt in the home. Do not eat soup or sauces in restaurants; they are too high in sodium. Always order the dressing on the side and ask if the

food can be prepared without the sauce. If you are using a packaged food, make sure the sodium content is not more than 400 mg, and make sure that this is the only sodium-extra food that you consume that day. In other words, limit your salt consumption to 300-400 mg per day in addition to the natural sodium found in all the unsalted produce and other dishes you eat each day.

8. Watch the Olive Oil! One tablespoon of olive oil has 120 calories (all oils do). One-quarter cup has 500 calories. Healthy salads are definitely a way of life for people who want to lose weight or improve health. However, many of the benefits of a salad are lost when the calorie count is increased ten-fold with oil. Flavored vinegars, fruit and nut-based dressings are definitely the way to go. Nuts and seeds, not oil, have shown dramatic protection against heart disease. We need to get more of our fats from these wholesome foods and less from processed oils. Oil is a fattening, low-nutrient food. If you eat something cooked with oil, make sure you do not use oil on your salad that day.

9. Six-A-Day...Not The Way! You have probably heard it's better to eat six small meals a day. That is not ideal. You simply will not need to eat that frequently once your body is well nourished with micronutrients. The body can more effectively detoxify and enhance cell repair when not constantly eating and digesting. Eating right removes cravings and reduces the sensations driving us to eat too frequently and too much. For most people who follow a high-nutrient diet-style, eating when truly hungry means eating three meals a day. For many, two meals and a snack is plenty of food.

10. The combination of processed foods and animal products should comprise less than 10 percent of your total calorie intake. For example, if you are a female eating 1,400-1,800 calories a day, only 150 calories should come from animal products or refined carbohydrate. If you are a male eating 1,800-2,400 calories a day, no more than 200 calories should come from these foods. The rest should come from natural plant foods.

# Exercises with food

If you are overwhelmed and don't know where or how to start, this is for you. Let's start putting some of the principles that you have learned into practice. These ten dietary exercises are the place to start. It is important that you think of these exercises in the same way that you think of exercises at the gym. When you go to the gym, you don't expect to suddenly build muscle; that takes time. You may not even enjoy going to the gym when you first start out. The enjoyment comes later, when you see your body starting to change.

Move down the exercise list. Perform each exercise for at least a week, and then move on to the next. You can still continue the prior exercises as you add additional exercise challenges on your journey to incredible health.

The most important element of these exercises is performing them every single day. Doing them daily will not only increase your enjoyment of healthful foods, but also will help you lose weight. In the beginning, you may continue eating some foods from your traditional diet, although you will probably be eating a lot less of them. Over time, you will be more comfortable eliminating your unhealthful food choices and replacing them with healthful ones because your palate will desire them.

A skill is a developed talent or ability, and being healthy is the result of several skills. The difficulty comes when you try to be proficient in all of those skills at once. Enjoying the taste of healthful food is a skill. Giving up old foods that you love in favor of new foods that you don't like requires multiple skills: abstinence and tolerance. These exercises isolate and target specific skill sets. They will help you avoid the anxiety that many feel when they give up their old way of eating all of a sudden. The method that I have developed is a purposeful and effective way to assist you in your transition to preferring a healthful approach to eating.

I also want you to keep a health journal; it has a proven record of enhancing success as documented in the scientific literature. Record your food intake, which exercises you are working on and your results. Review your health journal and make note of the transformation that has taken place as you go. Use the space in this book, or duplicate the pages in a notebook designed for that purpose. Check over your goals and update them if necessary and add any new goals that you might now have. For now, create a plan for the next 2 weeks on what your health goals are and how you want to accomplish these goals. Every two weeks make some new goals, log how much weight you lost (if that is one of your goals), how fit you've become and what other health-related accomplishments you've achieved. Keep track of your progress. Write down if you reached your goals and if not, what you plan to do better, so you can clearly see the benefits and results.

## EXERCISE 1

Eat one-half pound of cut up raw vegetables and one-half pound of low-calorie fruits each day.

Try to do this exercise at the same time each day. I recommend eating the fruit at breakfast and the raw vegetables in the afternoon before dinner. The important thing is to do this exercise close to mealtime and not when you have a full stomach. Remember, your lunch should be light enough, so you are really hungry before dinner. It will make dinner more enjoyable to eat it when you are really hungry.

The goal of this exercise is to eat a comfortable amount of raw vegetables, including tomatoes, red pepper, carrots, broccoli spears, celery, snow pea pods, and zucchini, and fruits, including fresh berries, cantaloupe, kiwi, and apple slices. Over time, see if you can comfortably increase the volume of food. Plus, if you want to eat more than a half of a pound of salad to begin dinner you can. You can use one of our healthy dressing recipes with these raw vegetables too, and you can even cut up the fruit and make a salad that has in it both fruits and lettuce, shredded cabbage, shredded carrots or beets, onion and tomato.

After eating all these raw vegetables and fruits, you may decide to eat less at dinner because you feel too full, but let that decision come naturally. Try not to overeat, but don't try to restrict yourself, either. Eat the amount that feels comfortable, and try to stop eating before you feel full. Stop when you're satisfied. Finding the difference between being satisfied and full is an important step in becoming a healthy eater.

❑ **Check here when you have completed EXERCISE 1 for at least a week**

## EXERCISE 2

The second exercise can be done at the same time as the first. While you are eating those fruits and vegetables, chew each mouthful until every piece of food is liquefied. This will take a considerable amount of time and will feel very different from how you are used to eating, but how you eat is very important. Eating slowly is the only way to gain all the nutrients that you want from the food. You can access the full nutrient load from the food by breaking open every single plant cell. Eating this way also will exercise your jaw and help you develop healthier gums and teeth. Remember: Chew, chew, and chew.

❑ **Check here when you have completed EXERCISE 2 for at least a week**

## EXERCISE 3

Take the half-pound of vegetables and half-pound of fruit that you are eating daily and increase them to one pound each per day. The pound of vegetables can be raw or cooked. Eating two salads daily—one of vegetables and one of fruit or whatever combination you feel like—is not too much. To help you meet your vegetable goal, eat a bowl of vegetable bean soup or a vegetable bean casserole each day. The recipes in Super Immunity can help you along the way. Try some of the delicious salad dressing recipes with your salads, or use them as dips for raw vegetables. One pound may seem like an overwhelmingly large amount of vegetables, but keep in mind one tomato can weigh half a pound, and other high water-content foods, such as cucumbers and peppers, add up the weight quickly. If you are starting to feel full, stop eating. Do not allow any of these exercises to encourage you to overeat or eat until discomfort.

❏ **Check here when you have completed EXERCISE 3 for at least two weeks**

## EXERCISE 4

As you add more volume to your diet, also change the types of fruits and vegetables that you are eating. Alternate at least two different fruits and two different vegetables in your diet each week. Also, I encourage you as part of this exercise to try a fruit or vegetable that you rarely eat or have never tried. This is a good opportunity to see the palate stretching in action as you realize that your tastes can change. Especially seek out fresh pomegranates, shallots, fresh parsley and dill, various mushrooms, and other leafy greens in stews and main dishes, such as collards, mustard greens and broccoli rabe. All these foods have powerful effects to prevent cancer and repair any cell damage that could have occurred in the past that could lead to cancer. Grocery stores today have plenty of variety in their produce departments that most likely contain something you've not yet discovered. Be adventurous; stretch your palate and your experience in an effort to have a more complete diet. Like all exercises, they require frequent practice in order to see results. Remember, it takes 15 times of eating a new food to develop a taste for it. This will also help give you better phytochemical variety, which has health benefits and helps rid you of toxic hunger.

❏ **Check here when you have completed EXERCISE 4 for a month**

## EXERCISE 5

Make a point to eat a light lunch or a light breakfast each day. Eating one lighter meal without snacking before the next meal, either lunch or dinner, will increase your true hunger before that meal. Over time, this will help to teach you what true hunger feels like. The main exercise target here is to see if you can get back in touch with sensations of "true hunger," differentiating the sensations from "toxic hunger." Be patient because it may take some time (even a few months) for toxic hunger to go away. However, this exercise of trying to eat two main meals and one lighter meal, with no snacking will help you get in touch with your hunger symptoms. The point here is that hunger is the best sauce, in other words it will greatly enhance the pleasure when you do eat. Try to link together an entire week of high-nutrient eating, with no snacking, so you can lose the toxic hunger symptoms and begin the pleasurable sensation of true hunger.

☐ **Check here when you have completed EXERCISE 5 for at least a week**

## EXERCISE 6

Reduce your consumption of animal products (meat, eggs, and dairy products) to no more than one serving every other day. That means if you have some animal product during the day, make the next day completely vegan. Eventually, reduce the size of the animal product servings so when you do use them, it is not more than a few ounces to flavor a stew, soup or dish. Use the high-nutrient recipes in Super Immunity to replace animal products in your menus.

☐ **Check here when you have completed EXERCISE 6 for at least two weeks**

## EXERCISE 7

Remove white flour, sugar, and other sweeteners from your diet. For this exercise, no artificial sweeteners or low calorie sweeteners are allowed either. This means using fewer processed foods. Store-purchased products should be 100 percent whole grain and contain no sweetening agents. Remember, wheat flour means white flour, it must say 100 percent whole wheat or 100 percent whole grains. Sweeteners and white flour promote cancer, so it is wise to avoid them or only use them very occasionally. Obviously, for this two week exercise, you are making a commitment to have no sugar or other sweetening agents such as honey or maple syrup or even stevia for a full 2 weeks. Think you can do it?

This exercise when continued for a few weeks helps recondition your taste to enjoy the subtle flavors and sweetness in fruits and vegetables. What most people do not realize is that the continual intake of a diet rich in sweeteners deadens ones taste buds, so simple foods like strawberries no longer taste sweet. The only thing sweet should be fresh fruit. The purpose of this exercise is to break your addiction to sweets, so you control your dietary choices, and no longer have cravings.

☐ **Check here when you have completed EXERCISE 7 for at least two weeks**

## EXERCISE 8

The base of the nutritarian diet is green vegetables. If you do not consume cooked green vegetables on a daily basis let's change that today. Not only should you have lots of raw greens as discussed in the earlier exercises, but also make sure you now eat a large serving of cooked greens too. Delicious, yet mild tasting, green vegetables include green beans, sugar-snap peas, zucchini, asparagus and artichokes as well as broccoli, kale and much more. They are all great cooked with onions, scallions, garlic and mushrooms. You can sauté them in water, tomato juice, or other veggie juice, or with coconut water and sliced pineapple for a Hawaiian flavor. You can stew them with beans and vegetable juice, or enjoy them just steamed plain with or without a dip. Try lots of the green-based main dishes from the recipe section of the book and keep track of your favorites.

☐ **Check here when you have completed EXERCISE 8 for at least two weeks**

## EXERCISE 9

Decreasing one's sodium can be one of the most difficult things to do because salt is so addictive and because it deadens your taste buds, making food taste bland for up to 3 months before they revitalize themselves. I want you to avoid any sodium that is not in natural produce, except for 300-400 mg a day. That means you eat all produce, but if you have a piece of store-bought whole grain bread, or some tomato sauce or ketchup, you have to read the label and measure the amount used so you don't go over that 300-400 mg level. That will keep the total sodium in your diet under 1000 mg a day. Commit to this for a full week. Sustain it longer or even better, continually if possible.

Remember to read labels as 80% of our sodium intake comes from pre-packaged foods rather than the salt shaker. Pay attention when eating your meals to the other flavors found in food besides saltiness. Increase the sourness and sweetness of your meals by using vinegars, lemon and fruits. Add interesting herbs and spices and no-salt spice mixtures. Then go back to a regular sodium day that you ate before the experiment a week later. Notice the difference in your taste buds. Record the experience of this experiment in your health journal. Then expand the number of days on a low sodium diet again focusing on the other flavors of foods rather than saltiness. Realize that your taste buds are being revitalized and will soon be able to taste things in a new way that will make unprocessed plant foods taste amazing. Again record your experiences in your health journal.

☐ **Check here when you have completed EXERCISE 9 for at least two weeks**

## EXERCISE 10

Research and find two restaurants in your area that will cater to your nutritarian diet-style. This exercise involves going out to eat and still remaining on your nutritarian diet in two different places over a two-week period. The first step is finding a restaurant that will have some healthy meal options. Calling ahead can be very helpful in this regard and you can ask questions on whether they will cater to your preferences. Many restaurants for breakfast offer fresh orange juice and oatmeal with raisins and fruit. For lunch and dinner, try to find a restaurant with a salad bar or even a market that has a salad bar and eating area. If they don't have a salad bar, order a double-size salad minus unhealthy items (cheese, bacon bits, etc.) and have the dressing on the side. Use only a touch of commercial dressing adding extra vinegar and lemon if you wish. See what vegetable options are on the menu, even if part of another dish and ask if you can have a double-sized portion of those. Make sure you clearly reiterate, not to use oil or salt and that you appreciate the staff for complying with your dietary requirements. You can always say, "doctor's orders". Avoid consuming soups in restaurants as they are almost always loaded with salt. It is also very important to ask the waiter not to bring the tempting bread basket to the table.

☐ **Check here when you have completed EXERCISE 10 for at least two weeks**

# Food Guide – Dietary Goals

Three sets of dietary goals are provided. You can track your progress in meeting these daily goals in the calendar section of this workbook.

**PREVENTION:** for those who wish to minimize their risk of infections and cancers

**AUTOIMMUNE:** these goals are for individuals who have an autoimmune disease

**CANCER:** if you have or have had cancer, aim for these goals

## DIETARY GOALS: PREVENTION

**Greens (and other non-starchy vegetables)**

- Eat at least one large salad each day, including 4-6 cups of raw leafy greens, plus 1-2 cups of other raw vegetables (carrots, snow peas, tomatoes, etc.).

- Also eat 3 cups per day of cooked vegetables, either steamed or included in other dishes.

- At least one cup of your daily vegetables (either cooked or raw) should be from the cruciferous family.

**Beans**

- Eat at least ½ cup of beans or lentils each day.

**Onions (and onion family members)**

- Eat ½ cup of vegetables from the onion family each day – these include onions, shallots, leeks, garlic, chives, and scallions.

**Mushrooms**

- Eat at least 8 ounces of mushrooms (cooked) each week (1 cup cooked).

**Berries (and other fruits)**

- Eat at least 1 cup of berries or pomegranate each day.

- Eat 2-5 additional servings of fruit each day.

**Seeds (and nuts and avocado)**

- Take 1 tablespoon of hemp, chia, or ground flaxseed each day.

- Eat nuts and seeds daily, but limit to 2-4 ounces/day (1 ounce/day if overweight).

- Avocado can be included in place of a nut/seed serving. One avocado is equivalent to about 1.5 ounces of nuts/seeds.

**Foods to Limit**

- Limit whole grains and starchy vegetables to 2-3 cups per day (1 cup/day if overweight) – beans are the most healthful carbohydrate source.

- Limit dried fruit to 1/4 cup per day (1/4 cup/week if overweight).

- Limit poultry, eggs, fish, and dairy to 12 ounces per week.

- Limit oils to 3 tablespoons of olive oil per week.

- Limit white potatoes to 2 cups per week.

- Limit added sodium to 300-400 mg per day.

**Foods to Avoid**

- Red and processed meats (beef, pork, cold cuts, etc.)

- Sugars and sweets

- White rice and white flour products

- Processed foods

## DIETARY GOALS: AUTOIMMUNE DISEASE

**Greens (and other non-starchy vegetables)**

- Eat at least one large salad each day, including 4-6 cups of raw leafy greens daily, plus 1-2 cups of other raw vegetables (carrots, snow peas, tomatoes, etc.).

- Also eat 3 cups per day of cooked vegetables, either steamed or included in other dishes.

- At least 2 cups of your daily vegetables (either cooked or raw) should be from the cruciferous family.

- Often, have some of your vegetables in the form of fresh vegetable juices and blended salads to increase phytochemical absorption.

**Beans**

- Eat at least ½ cup of beans or lentils each day.

**Onions (and onion family members)**

- Eat ½ cup of vegetables from the onion family each day – these include onions, shallots, leeks, garlic, chives, and scallions.

**Mushrooms**

- Eat 2-4 ounces of mushrooms (cooked) each day (¼-½ cup cooked).

**Berries (and other fruits)**

- Eat at least 1 cup of berries or pomegranate each day.

- Eat 2-5 additional servings of fruit each day.

**Seeds (and nuts and avocado)**

- Take 1 tablespoon of hemp, chia, or ground flaxseed each day.

- Eat nuts and seeds daily, but limit to 2-4 ounces/day (1 ounce/day if overweight).

- Avocado can be included in place of a nut/seed serving. One avocado is equivalent to about 1.5 ounces of nuts/seeds.

**Foods to Limit**
- Avoid wheat. Limit whole grains and starchy vegetables to 2-3 cups per day (1 cup/day if overweight) – beans are the most healthful carbohydrate source.
- Limit dried fruit to 1/4 cup per day (1/4 cup/week if overweight).
- Limit white potatoes to 2 cups per week.

**Foods to Avoid**
- All animal products
- All oils
- Wheat
- Added sodium
- Sugars and sweets

**Special dietary considerations for inflammatory bowel diseases**

Inflammatory bowel diseases (IBD) – ulcerative colitis and Crohn's disease – are autoimmune diseases in which the intestinal lining is the site of the autoimmune attack. I recommend certain alterations to the autoimmune dietary protocol for these conditions, in order to maximize phytochemical intake while avoiding irritating the inflamed intestinal lining:

**Phase 1**
(active disease with blood, typically more than 6 bowel movements daily): In the midst of an IBD flare-up, the diet should be mostly cooked vegetables, plus gently heated green juices. Fresh fruit should be limited to papaya in this phase.

**Phase 2**
(mildly active disease, no blood, fewer than 6 bowel movements per day): Introduce fresh raw vegetable juices (4-8 ounces/day) and blended salads (green smoothies – blend raw greens with avocado and banana). The diet should still be primarily cooked vegetables, adding some tofu, high omega-3 eggs, or a small (3 ounce) serving of fish daily. Limit fruit to one non-citrus fruit with each meal.

**Phase 3**
(normal stool, 3 or fewer bowel movements per day – long-term diet): Include more raw vegetables and fresh fruits, but continue to use juices and blended salads.

I also recommend occasional fasting to rest the intestinal wall and promote healing for my IBD patients. Start out with a one-day fast of water and green juices, then try a one-day water fast. The following week, try a two-day fast. Progress gradually until you are completing a 3-5 day fast, once each month.

For IBD, follow the supplement recommendations for autoimmune diseases.

## DIETARY GOALS: CANCER

### Greens (and other non-starchy vegetables)

- Eat at least one large salad each day, including 4-6 cups of raw leafy greens daily, plus 1-2 cups of other raw vegetables (carrots, snow peas, tomatoes, etc.).

- Drink 8-10 ounces of fresh vegetable juice each day, preferably including greens.

- Also eat 3 cups per day of cooked vegetables, either steamed or included in other dishes.

- At least 3 cups of your daily vegetables (either cooked or raw) should be from the cruciferous family.

### Beans

- Eat 1 cup of beans or lentils each day

### Onions (and onion family members)

- Eat 1 cup of vegetables from the onion family each day – these include onions, shallots, leeks, garlic, chives, and scallions.

### Mushrooms

- Eat 2-4 ounces of mushrooms (cooked) each day (¼-½ cup cooked).

### Berries (and other fruit)

- Eat at least 2 cups of berries or pomegranate each day.

- Eat 2-4 additional servings of fruit each day.

### Nuts/seeds

- Take 1 tablespoon of hemp, chia, or ground flaxseed each day.

- Eat nuts and seeds daily, but limit to 2-4 ounces/day (1 ounce/day if overweight).

- Avocado can be included in place of a nut/seed serving. One avocado is equivalent to about 1.5 ounces of nuts/seeds.

### Limited foods

- Limit whole grains and starchy vegetables to 1 cup per day – preferentially choose beans as a carbohydrate source to minimize glycemic effects.

- Limit dried fruit to 1/4 cup per week to minimize glycemic effects.

### Foods to Avoid

- All animal products
- All oils
- White potatoes
- Added sodium
- Sugars and sweets

## SUPPLEMENT GUIDE

### Prevention

- Multivitamin and mineral supplement (no vitamin A, vitamin E, beta-carotene, folic acid, or copper)

- Vitamin D (according to 25(OH)D blood level; if you have not had your blood tested, 2000 IU is reasonable)

- Low dose omega-3 supplement (150-300 mg DHA+EPA per day)

### Autoimmune

- Multivitamin and mineral supplement (no vitamin A, vitamin E, beta-carotene, folic acid, or copper)

- Additional Vitamin D (according to 25(OH)D blood level; if you have not had your blood tested, a total of 2000 IU is reasonable)

- High dose omega-3 supplement with 1000-3000 mg EPA per day

- High dose probiotic, two capsules twice daily

- Natural anti-inflammatory substances: turmeric, ginger, quercetin

### Cancer

- Multivitamin and mineral supplement (no vitamin A, vitamin E, beta-carotene, folic acid, or copper)

- Vitamin D (according to 25(OH)D blood level; if you have not had your blood tested, 2000 IU is reasonable)

- Low dose omega-3 supplement (150-300 mg DHA+EPA per day)

- Mixed mushroom supplement

- Green tea supplement

- Resveratrol supplement

## EXERCISE GUIDE

Exercise is indispensable for overall health and building Super Immunity - people who exercise regularly have fewer colds that are shorter and less severe compared to sedentary individuals.[47] As soon as you begin to lose some weight and start feeling better, usually once the withdrawal phase of the first week is over, start to increase your physical exercise intensity, and do more than just walk. Exercise more vigorously and do something vigorous every day – vigorous exercise is associated with longevity. For example, do jumping jacks for 3 minutes, or jog in place. At the beginning, just jog with your feet hardly lifting off the ground, but as the weeks and months progress, not only should you increase your duration, but as you pick your feet and knees up high off the ground,

you can increase the intensity of the effort. Do something every day, increasing the minutes of intense exercise you can tolerate.

It is also important for your long-term health to not sit all day long. Even if you are exercising regularly, it is still important to limit your sitting during the day. Try to stand when talking on the phone and put your laptop or paperwork elevated on a counter and work standing up part of the day as well. Look for opportunities during the day to walk extra flights of stairs. I sometimes place my laptop on a large overturned pot on my kitchen counter to bring it to a comfortable standing height. Limit sitting, maximize motion and try to be conscious of incorporating fitness into your everyday life, every single day.

## EXERCISE 1: CHAIR SQUATS

Use a chair as a measuring tool to know how far to bend at the knees for your squats. The chair should be behind you with your feet parallel to your shoulders and arms at your side. Bend at the knee until your buttocks lightly touch the seat. Raise straightened arms to the level of your shoulders as you bend your knees. Repeat this.

*Side note: If the exercise is too difficult, you may place a pillow or a phone book to raise the seat height.*

## EXERCISE 2: ONE LEGGED TOE RAISES

This exercise is preferably done on a stair. Use the stair rail as balance. Eventually this exercise is to be done one leg at a time (described below), but initially use both feet simultaneously. Hold on to the railing for balance, especially if doing one foot at a time. The ball of your foot should be at the edge of the stair so the heel can drop down lower. Raise and drop your heel about fifteen times to twenty times. Then, switch to the opposite foot and repeat.

## EXERCISE 3: STEP LUNGES

Start with your feet together and take a large step forward outward from your body and drop the rear knee towards the floor. Remember you do not have to touch the floor with the knee. Aim for 10 steps on each leg alternating legs with every step you take. At the beginning start gradually without bending too low.

## EXERCISE 4: JUMP LUNGES

Take a large jump to the right side with your right leg. As you jump, bring your left elbow down to your right knee; keeping your left foot raised at a 90 degree angle behind you making you balance on your right foot. Bend down and try to touch your left elbow with your right knee. Then, jump to the left with the left foot and repeat the exercise in a rhythmic motion jumping from side to side.

## EXERCISE 5: SUPERMAN SWIM

Use an exercise mat. Lie stomach down on the mat with your arms raised above your head like Superman flying through the air. Then, raise your left arm, head, and right leg high, all at the same time. Then, stretch. Slowly lower your left arm, head and right leg until they are resting on the mat. Repeat with the right arm and left leg alternating sides.

## EXERCISE 6: BACK EXTENSIONS

Lay face down on your exercise mat. Place your arms at your sides parallel to your body. Now, only lift your upper body off the floor. Raise and pull your upper body as far as you can away from the mat keeping your arms resting at your sides and hold for three seconds. Then, come back down so your upper body is resting on the floor. Repeat the exercise.

## EXERCISE 7: DANCING IN PLACE

Dance, hop and jump up and down staying in place. Move your arms, twist your body and jump just like you were dancing. Jump on two feet. Then, if you can advance, jump on one foot and then the other. The beginner starts with a dancing motion shifting weight from side to side as they bounce up and down. Then as you advance rock and lift of the ground as you dance with a small hop.

## EXERCISE 8: JOGGING IN PLACE

Pick up your knees high to increase the intensity of the exercise as you advance. Go for the full 3 to 4 minutes equal to one song.

## EXERCISE 9: PLANKS

Support yourself on your feet and hands like in the stretched out position ready to do a push-up. Then, raise your right leg back straight behind and as high as possible. Bring your right leg back to the starting position. Then, repeat with your left leg. Do this 20 times with each leg. Try to advance the exercise so you lift the opposite arm off the ground stretching it up and forward at the same time as the leg, similar to the Superman swim.

## EXERCISE 10: LEG RAISES

Lay with your back flat on the floor keeping your arms at your side and your legs together straight out in front of you. Then, raise both legs off the floor from 12 to 24 inches. Hold; bring your legs down touching the ground lightly. Repeat 10 to 20 times.

## EXERCISE 11: TWISTING AB CRUNCHES

Lay with your back on the floor, knees bent and fingers interlocked behind your head with your elbows out. Your hands support the head. Crunch your stomach so your right elbow and left knee meet. Bring your knee and elbow back to the floor and repeat with your left elbow, right knee. Do this on each side 10 to 20 times.

# FAQ

 **Red wine: heart healthy?**

Moderate drinking has been associated with a lower incidence of coronary heart disease in more than forty prospective studies. This only applies to moderate drinking – defined as one drink or less per day for women, and two drinks or less for men. Excess alcohol is of course harmful – more than moderate alcohol intake is associated with increased fat around the waist and other potential problems, especially increased incidence of cancer.[48]

As a result of these studies, alcohol has been touted as "heart-healthy". However, alcohol does not actually have any beneficial effect on the cardiovascular system; it only inhibits the blood's clotting mechanisms, similar to aspirin. Researchers have found that this interference with blood clotting does grant some protective effect against heart attacks, but this protective effect is valuable only in a person or population consuming a dangerous, heart-disease-promoting diet. Eating a diet rich in unrefined plant foods is health-promoting and effective at preventing heart disease, and then the risks associated with thinning the blood such as

hemorrhagic stroke and stomach and intestinal bleeding are not increased. Thinning the blood with alcohol or aspirin has potentially life-threatening risks.

Alcohol consumption also leads to mild withdrawal sensations the next day that are commonly mistaken for hunger. This leads people to eat more than is genuinely necessary, resulting in weight gain. One glass of wine per day is likely insignificant, but I advise against higher levels of alcohol consumption, as it may lead to health problems. For example, even moderate alcohol consumption is linked to higher rates of breast cancer and also higher rates of breast cancer recurrence after diagnosis[49] – since breast cancer is the second leading cause of death in women (second to cardiovascular disease), it is best for women to minimize alcohol consumption in order to reduce these risks. Alcohol is also associated with cardiac arrhythmias, which may lead to sudden cardiac death.[50]

Red wine is the alcoholic beverage most often associated with reduced cardiovascular risk. Red wine does contains some beneficial compounds such as flavonoids and resveratrol, a potent antioxidant in the skin of grapes associated with a number of health benefits. Of course, grapes, raisins, berries, and other plant foods also contain these beneficial compounds. It is not necessary to drink wine to obtain these phytochemicals.

And lastly, the sensible reason the American Heart Association does not recommend people drink wine or other alcoholic beverages is stated below

> *Drinking more alcohol increases such dangers as alcoholism, high blood pressure, obesity, stroke, breast cancer, suicide and accidents. Also, it's not possible to predict in which people alcoholism will become a problem. Given these and other risks, the American Heart Association cautions people NOT to start drinking if they do not already drink alcohol. Consult your doctor on the benefits and risks of consuming alcohol in moderation.*[51]

I agree, drinking alcohol or one cup of wine is not a major risk, nor is it a major health asset; however, if consumed in excess, it can develop into a major health risk. Overall, it is safer to eat a diet that will not permit heart disease rather than to rely on alcohol to decrease the potential of blood to clot. The bottom line is that the moderate drinking of alcohol is only an advantage to those who consume an unhealthy diet. There are no protective effects in low risk individuals consuming healthful, plant based diets with resultant low cholesterol levels. It is wiser to avoid the detrimental effects of alcohol completely and protect yourself from heart disease with nutritional excellence.

 **Q Do I need to take vitamins?**

**A** Since most people's diets are not ideal and individual absorption and utilization varies from person to person, it makes sense to recommend that all people take a high-quality multivitamin/multimineral to avoid micronutrient deficiencies. It is important to ensure adequate levels of essential micronutrients, such as vitamin D, vitamin B12, zinc, iodine, and DHA. The judicious use of supplements can be utilized to offer nutritional insurance, but many nutritional supplements can bring about more harm than good - more is not always better. People can easily hurt themselves with too much supplementation.

Typical multivitamins may expose you to extra nutrients that you do not need and can even be toxic. Excessive quantities of some vitamins and minerals can be toxic or have long term negative health effects. Some forms are more absorbable and useful to our bodies then others. The goal is to supplement intelligently. The following are potentially dangerous supplements that are routinely added to most multivitamins.

**Beta-carotene, Vitamin A, and Vitamin E.** There are risks associated with consuming more beta-carotene and vitamin A than what we naturally receive in our diets. Ingesting vitamin A or beta-carotene in isolation from supplements can potentially increase cancer risk by interfering with the absorption of other carotenoids with anti-cancer properties, like lutein and lycopene.[52] Beta-carotene supplements are poor substitutes for the broad assortment of carotenoid compounds found in plants. It is much safer and healthier to consume food sources of beta-carotene, like spinach, kale and carrots, which also contain several additional carotenoids as well as hundreds of other beneficial phytochemicals.

Since beta-carotene gets converted into vitamin A by your body, there is no reason a person eating a reasonably healthy diet should require any extra vitamin A. There is solid research revealing that supplemental vitamin A induces calcium loss in the urine, contributing to osteoporosis.[53] Too much vitamin A from supplements during pregnancy is associated with cardiac birth defects.[54] On top of these risks, a recent meta-analysis found an increased risk of mortality in people who took supplemental vitamin A, beta-carotene, or vitamin E.[55]

**Iron and copper.** Iron and copper serve vital biological functions, but as we age excess amounts of these metals may build up and become toxic. The most common culprits of iron and copper excess are red meat and multivitamins. Iron is crucial for oxygen transport, and both iron and copper are essential for the proper function of several chemical reactions in several of the body's cells and tissues. The human body evolved to store excess iron and copper to fuel these reactions in case of extreme conditions like bleeding or famine. However, their accumulation over time may be detrimental because both metals are involved in generating oxidative stress, a byproduct of energy production, which contributes to chronic diseases – specifically cardiovascular disease and brain disorders like Alzheimer's Disease.[56] There are, however, appropriate times to supplement with iron: when there is a deficiency or an increased biological need, such as in pregnancy.

**Folic acid.** The synthetic folic acid found in supplements is chemically different from food folate, which is abundant in green vegetables like spinach, romaine lettuce, collards, and broccoli. Folate is especially important for women of childbearing age, to prevent against birth defects. However, women who take synthetic folic acid in multivitamins or prenatal vitamins may be at increased risk of breast cancer.[57] Folic acid supplementation also raises the risk of prostate and colorectal cancers.[58]

Luckily, we don't need to get folic acid from vitamins, because folate is plentiful in green vegetables. Folate in its natural form protects against breast and prostate cancers.[59] Getting folate from food ensures that we do not get too much, since it comes naturally packaged in balance with other micronutrients.

In spite of the huge volume of solid information documenting the deleterious effects of these supplements, it is still difficult to find a multivitamin that does not contain these substances. For more information on potentially harmful supplements, please visit http://www.drfuhrman.com/library/harmful_vitamins.aspx. For recommendations on appropriate vitamins and supplements, please visit my Vitamin Advisor (http://www.drfuhrman.com/shop/VAdvisor.aspx). Remember, dietary supplements are indeed supplements, not substitutes for a healthy diet.

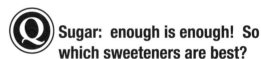 **Sugar: enough is enough! So which sweeteners are best?**

Primates are the only mammals that can sense sweet tastes. Fruit is an essential part of the human diet. We have such a large area of our tongue to taste sweets and a natural inclination to enjoy them. Our natural sweet tooth has a purpose – sweets from fresh fruits and other plant substances provide us not just with carbohydrates for energy but also with a large assortment of phytochemicals and other substances that prevent illness.

Unfortunately, in our society, our natural primate desire for sweets is typically satisfied by consuming products containing refined sugars – candy bars, soda, and ice cream – instead of fresh fruit. The American Heart Association released a statement in 2009 reporting that the typical American adult now consumes an unbelievable 22 teaspoons of added sugar each day. More troubling was the fact that teens were found to consume even more added sugar – 34 teaspoons per day.[60]

Refined sugars cause us to be malnourished in direct proportion to how much of them we consume. They are partially to blame for the high cancer and heart attack rates we see in America. Refined sugars include table sugar (sucrose), milk sugar (lactose), honey, brown sugar, high-fructose corn syrup, molasses, corn sweeteners, maple syrup, and fruit juice concentrates. To your body they are all the same: empty calories. Even the fruit juices that many children drink are a poor quality food with no significant nutrient density. Juices don't compare to the real fruit. White rice, white bread, and pasta are no different than sugar once we put them in our mouths. They are deficient in nutrients and are absorbed too rapidly. They contain empty calories, just like sugar, raising our blood sugar and insulin levels. Also the lack of nutrients in these refined foods means that these foods will not satisfy our appetites. This leads to overeating which contributes to obesity, diabetes, cardiovascular disease, and cancers.

Refined sugars and nutrient-depleted processed sweets – deficient in fiber, phytonutrients, vitamins and minerals – are a poor substitute for fresh fruit. These foods are harmful, but even more harmful is that we are missing hundreds of valuable phytochemicals when we eat these nutrient-deficient desserts instead of fresh fruit.

Fresh fruits are natural, nutrient-rich, health-promoting foods. Researchers have discovered substances in fruits, especially blueberries and strawberries, that have unique effects on preventing aging and deterioration of the brain.[61] Adding more fresh fruit to the diet can decrease the risk of diabetes.[62] Some fruits, especially blueberries, are rich in anthocyanins

and other compounds that have anti-aging effects.[63] Apple consumption is associated with decreased risk of colorectal cancer.[64] Eating citrus fruits decreases the risk of all cancers of the digestive tract.[65] Overall fruit consumption has been shown in numerous studies to offer our strongest protection against several cancers: oral and esophageal, lung, prostate, colorectal, and pancreatic cancer.[66]

How much fruit your children eat is also a strong determinant of their future health. A sixty-year study of about 5,000 participants found that those who were in the highest quartile of fruit consumption during childhood were found to have 38% lower incidence of all types of cancer as adults.[67]

Eating fruit instead of empty-calorie refined sugar is vital to your health and longevity. Sadly, according to the American Heart Association, Americans typically eat less than 2 servings of fruit per day. I recommend 4-6 servings of these nutrient-dense treats per day for excellent health.

In our house, not only do we enjoy fruit in its natural state, but we also whip up frozen fruits to make fantastic sorbets and creamy desserts. Do you think that your sweet tooth can't be satisfied by fruit? You can make delicious desserts without using refined sugars. Try this one: a little dried mango, soaked overnight in soy or hemp milk, blended in a high quality blender with frozen mango, a little lemon, and shredded coconut for a real treat for the entire family. You can substitute many other fruits in place of the mango.

**Where's the beef?**

 For years, the USDA Food Pyramid has suggested we consume beef and other animal products in order to get our protein. The USDA suggests approximately 600 calories of beef per day. Instead, remember that vegetables, beans and seeds are also high in protein, so there is no essential need to have animal products at every meal. In fact, broccoli has more protein per calorie than steak. Think about it… cows are vegan, as are gorillas and horses. Trying to lose weight or reduce your cholesterol? Think Greens for health and for building lean muscles. For great health we need to get more protein from nutrient-rich plant sources such as greens, beans, seeds and nuts and less from animal products.

 **Not milk?**

An average cow produces 25 times more milk per year than just fifty years ago. Are cows getting bigger? Sure we all need calcium for strong bones, but calcium is just a small part of the story, hundreds of other nutrients are also needed for healthy bones and the quantity of vegetables consumed, not dairy, is the best predictor of bone health. Remember, green vegetables not only have plenty of calcium, but have the other necessary nutrients that build bones. For great health, we should get more calcium from nutrient-rich plant sources such as greens, beans, seeds and nuts and less from dairy products. Our body needs thousands of discovered and undiscovered nutrients that work synergistically. A higher intake of milk is linked to a higher incidence of both prostate cancer and ovarian cancer.[68]

 **Why limit whole grains and starchy vegetables?**

Intact whole grains (such as wild rice, brown rice, quinoa, oats, barley) are healthful natural foods that contain beneficial phytochemicals. But be wary of processed whole grain products, such as whole grain cold cereals, breads, and pastas. The phrase "whole grain" on a packaged food label does not mean "health-promoting food." When the whole grain is ground down into flour, there is a decrease in nutrient content and an increase in glycemic load compared to the original intact grain. For example, whole wheatberries (intact grains) cooked in water are more nutritious than 100% whole wheat bread (a whole grain processed food). Also, high temperature cooking of grains and starches (as in making breads and cold cereals) produces dietary toxins called acrylamides, which should be minimized. Cooking intact grains in water is the most healthful way to prepare them. Starchy vegetables are also healthful foods, but they have greater glycemic load and less fiber and resistant starch than beans, and have the potential to promote weight gain or limit weight loss for some people.

For those with cancer, heart disease or diabetes or who are overweight, limit whole grains and starchy vegetables to one serving or one cup daily—for example, one corn on the cob, one sweet potato, a cup of butternut squash, or a cup of oatmeal. Intact whole grains and starchy vegetables are good carbohydrate sources, but beans are the ideal carbohydrate source.

# TEST YOUR KNOWLEDGE

1.  Dr. Fuhrman's health equation for excellent health is Health = _____ divided by calories.

2.  G-BOMBS is an acronym to help you remember the most powerful immune-supporting, anti-cancer foods.  What are they?

    _____  _____  _____  _____  _____

3.  List 3 items at or near the top of the caloric density list and 3 items at or near the bottom of the caloric density list.

    _____  _____  _____

    _____  _____  _____

4.  _____ vegetables contain glucosinolates, which when the vegetables are chopped are chewed are converted into powerful anti-cancer compounds called isothiocyanates.

5.  _____ and _____ are two of the few foods that contain aromatase inhibitors, which block the production of estrogen.

6.  Give at least 2 reasons why eating a lot a fish in order to supposedly get their healthy fatty acid benefits can backfire and cause your health to suffer.

    _____  _____

7.  List 3 plant foods that are high in omega-3 fatty acids

    _____  _____  _____

8. Dietary protein, especially animal protein, increases circulating levels of a hormone called _____, which is associated with several cancers.

9. What is angiogenesis and why is it important for tumor growth?

   _____

10. List 5 foods that contain natural angiogenesis inhibitors.

   _____   _____   _____   _____   _____

11. Which two types of vegetables need to be adequately chopped, crushed, or chewed, in order to form anti-cancer compounds?

   _____   _____

12. Which is the most healthful starch source?
    a. Whole wheat pasta
    b. White bread
    c. Beans
    d. Intact whole grains
    e. White potatoes

13. Beans are rich in _____, which is broken down by gut bacteria into colon-protective short chain fatty acids.

14. List three common ingredients in multivitamin supplements that could potentially cause harm.

   _____   _____   _____

15. If one follows a completely vegetarian/vegan diet without fortified foods and doesn't work outdoors, which two important vitamins should be supplemented?

   _____   _____

16. Why are nuts and seeds more healthful than olive oil as fat sources?

   _____

17. We should limit the amount of white potato that we eat, primarily because it has a high

    _____ .

18. List 5 cruciferous vegetables.

    _____   _____   _____   _____   _____

19. It is appropriate to take a probiotic supplement after taking _____.

20. List 3 important functions of healthy gut bacteria.

    _____   _____   _____

21. Antibiotics are not helpful for most sore throats, sinus congestion, and bronchitis cases
    because _____ .

22. Describe what toxic hunger is. Give three common symptoms that occur during toxic hunger.

    _____

    _____   _____   _____

23. List 4 foods that are high in plant-protein and can easily replace the animal protein one might
    be consuming right now.

    _____   _____   _____   _____

24. Sixty-two percent of calories in the standard American diet come from _____.

25. How is a bagel similar to a piece of chicken?

    _____

# THE LAST WORD

As long as you are alive, you can improve your health and prolong your life. Our health is our most precious and important possession we have and we should never give up our efforts to improve and maintain excellent health. We graduate from school; high school, college, even professional school (such as medical school) and the most important information we should have learned to protect our life and health destiny is not imparted to us. Social and economic forces acting against healthy eating, as well as the addictive nature of unhealthy foods, have taken over the minds and actions of most Americans. Slow suicide from overeating low-nutrient food is the norm.

I am here to tell you that my more than 25 years of experience helping people regain their health has taught me that healthy living is a blessing that makes life more pleasurable and fun. Plus, food doesn't taste that good once you are in the coffin. Congratulations on your efforts to better your health. We are on this road to better health together. Society's norms, with a reliance on drugs and the disease-promoting properties of the standard American diet have negative influences on our health. By working together and supporting each other we can achieve better health, make what we eat taste great and enjoy a better quality of life.

**Visit me at DrFuhrman.com**

Consider joining our member center for more support and camaraderie.

Follow our blog conversations at DiseaseProof.com

**I LOOK FORWARD TO HEARING ABOUT YOUR SUCCESS AND HOPE YOU ACHIEVE SUPER IMMUNITY AND EXCELLENT HEALTH.**

# Answers to 'Test Your Knowledge' Questions

1. Nutrients

2. Greens, Beans, Onions, Mushrooms, Berries, Seeds

3. High caloric density foods: oil, potato chips/French fries, meat, cheese, white bread. Low caloric density foods: green vegetables, non-starchy non-green vegetables, fresh fruit, beans

4. Cruciferous

5. Mushrooms, pomegranate

6. Two reasons why eating fish to get their healthy fatty acids can cause your health to suffer: 1-fish contains pollutants such as mercury that can be detrimental to health , 2-fish is still animal protein, which is high in calories and low in micronutrients, and will tend to raise cholesterol and IGF-1 levels. Elevated IGF-1 levels are associated with increased cancer risk.

7. Walnuts, chia seeds, hemp seeds, flaxseeds

8. IGF-1 (Insulin-like growth factor-1)

9. Angiogenesis is the formation of new blood vessels, and it is important for tumor growth because tumors must acquire a blood supply in order to grow and become dangerous.

10. Five of the following: Mushrooms, black rice, cinnamon, grapes, turmeric, ginger, citrus fruits, berries, peppers, cocoa, cruciferous vegetables, tea, soybeans, the onion family, flaxseed, spinach, pomegranate, tomato

11. The onion family and cruciferous vegetables

12. C. Beans

13. Resistant starch

14. Three of the following: Vitamin A, beta-carotene, vitamin E, folic acid, copper

15. Vitamin B12, vitamin D

16. Nuts and seeds are whole foods – they contain fiber and phytochemicals in addition to fat. Olive oil is a processed food that is 100% fat.

17. Glycemic load

18. Five of the following: Arugula, cauliflower, cabbage, bok choy, collards, rutabaga, broccoli, horseradish, turnips, broccoli rabe, kale, turnip greens, broccolini, kohlrabi, watercress, Brussels sprouts, mustard greens, radishes

19. Antibiotics

20. Three of the following: supplement the digestive process, produce vitamins, short-chain fatty acids, and proteins utilized by the body, protect against overgrowth of pathogenic bacteria and yeasts, strengthen immune function, create beneficial nutrients that prevent weight gain.

21. These conditions are most often caused by viruses, and antibiotics do not kill viruses.

22. Toxic hunger is the name for the sensations most people mistakenly consider hunger. Toxic hunger is a constellation of symptoms that illustrates a physical addiction to an unhealthy diet. They are signs of the body's need to detoxify during the heightened cleansing available after digestion ceases. Symptoms of toxic hunger include headaches, weakness, stomach cramping, lightheadedness, esophageal spasms, growling stomach, and irritability.

23. Four of the following: seeds (sunflower, hemp, sesame, pumpkin, etc.), nuts, beans, and green vegetables.

24. Processed foods

25. Both a bagel and a piece of chicken are high in calories and low in micronutrients. Neither contains a significant amount of antioxidants or phytochemicals. Plus they both raise hormones that promote cancer: a bagel will increase insulin levels and a piece of chicken will increase IGF-1.

# Your Super Immunity Workbook

As you embark on your new dietary journey, keep in mind that there are three vital components to high-level health. Each of the three components—nutritional, physical, and social—must be considered.

Nutritional component—Make every calorie count as you strive for maximum nutrition. The Immunity Solution provides all of the information you need.

Physical component—Make physical exercise a part of your normal routine. Joining a gym is a great bonus, but learn to take advantage of all of your opportunities to exercise—such as taking the stairs instead of the elevator and when possible walking instead of riding. You may find that exercise is easier and more pleasurable as your health improves and you start losing weight. Remember to limit sitting. Try to work part of the day standing up.

Social component—Develop the confidence and self-esteem necessary to deal with unhealthful influences. A healthy mindset is a prerequisite for a healthy lifestyle, and the best way to develop it is to surround yourself with people who engage in and support your health.

Over time, your tastes and food preferences will change. You become more comfortable eating high-nutrient foods, and it will become second nature—it will become the way you prefer to eat. This is a high-nutrient program, not a calorie-counting one.

Use the calendar space in this book to check off your dietary and exercise goals. Keep track of your progress. Write down if you reached your goals and if not and how you plan to do better, so you can clearly see the benefits and results.

## YOUR CURRENT HEALTH SNAPSHOT:

Now let's get a current snapshot of who you are and your current health statistics so that you can track your soon-to-be amazing path to incredible health and vitality.

Name: _____

Age: _____

Start Date with Dr. Fuhrman's teachings: _____

Starting Weight: _____

Waist Measurement: (at umbilicus) _____

Blood Pressure:_____

Medications/Supplements you are currently taking: _____

_____

_____

List any health issues you would like to be helped by this program:

_____

_____

_____

_____

_____

**BLOOD LEVELS**

| | Your levels | My recommendations |
|---|---|---|
| Total cholesterol | _____ | Less than 150 mg/dl |
| LDL cholesterol | _____ | Less than 100 mg/dl |
| Triglycerides | _____ | Less than 150 mg/dl |
| Vitamin D (25(OH)D) | _____ | 30-50 ng/ml |
| Fasting glucose | _____ | Less than 100 mg/dl |
| If diabetic, HbA1C | _____ | Less than 6 |

**ADDITIONAL LEVELS RELEVANT TO OTHER CONDITIONS**

_____

_____

_____

**CURRENT PHOTO**

# FINDING YOUR MOTIVATION

Starting a new program is both exciting and difficult. As humans we naturally want what is best for us, yet we also fear change. To overcome this fear you need to solidify your motivations for wanting to change your current lifestyle to a more vibrant and healthy one. Your motivations are the fuel to light the fire that is required for successful change from your current health habits to the healthiest habits that will propel you to a new level of health that you never dreamt was possible. With every great achievement comes some sacrifice and struggle and when we are struggling it's very helpful to have reminders as to why we are changing and what matters to us most.

**On a scale of 1 to 10, rate the most compelling reasons you have for eating healthfully:**

_____ I want to recover from or improve the symptoms of a chronic autoimmune illness, such as multiple sclerosis, rheumatoid arthritis, lupus, or inflammatory bowel disease.

_____ I want to protect myself frequent bouts of colds, flu, and other infectious diseases.

_____ I want to protect myself from cancer.

_____ I want to prevent the deterioration in health, physical, and mental abilities that are typically considered a normal part of aging.

_____ I want to lose weight and look and feel better.

_____ I want to increase my energy and reduce fatigue.

_____ I want to improve the health of my family.

_____ I want to improve my physical fitness.

_____ I want to have better digestion.

_____ I want to have better sexual enjoyment and performance.

_____ I want to look and feel younger.

_____ I want to have a better emotional outlook on life.

_____ I want to live longer.

_____ I want to live without medical interference and hospitalizations.

_____ I want to avoid surgery or prescription medication.

_____ I want to reduce my dependency on medication.

_____ I want to save money on health care and prescription drugs.

Other reasons: _____

_____

_____

_____

Each time you encounter some difficulty with the eating-style described in these materials, each time you want to revert back to your old ways of eating, each time you slip-up on the program, each time you believe great health is unattainable for you, come back and look at this page.

# CREATING YOUR FUTURE WITH GOALS

Now we are going to take your motivations a step further and create some specific goals to generate crystal clear targets for you to strive for. By writing down specifically what you want, you put into motion the forces that are necessary for achieving your desires.

Well-constructed goals literally create the future in advance. The formula for creating successful goals is that they need to be specific, time dependent and they must have clear and measurable outcomes. For instance, "I want to look great and lose weight" does not meet the criteria of a well-constructed goal. A better example would be "I want to lose 20 pounds in the next 6 weeks and be able fit into the size 6 jeans I wore in college." This second example is specific, has a timeline and a measurable outcome by which you can determine whether you have achieved your goal or not.

You can have all the knowledge and know all of the techniques but if you don't have a target to drive towards or compelling reasons why you are doing something then it is less likely you are going to get the most out of yourself. So alongside your goals you need to write down why you want to achieve them. You need to get absolutely clear on this. The why provides the fuel for you to accomplish your aspirations.

Many people erroneously believe that it's only a matter of willpower to change one's unhealthy habits to obtain a new and vibrant healthy lifestyle. Willpower is an unreliable emotional fuel that usually putters out over a short period of time. To be successful at making life long healthy changes you need knowledge, techniques, and a well-constructed strategic plan to put the knowledge and techniques into action. Key parts of that strategic plan are your goals. So, list below at least 5 health-related goals and the reasons why you want to achieve them. Then review them on a scheduled basis, perhaps every week or maybe even every night. Lastly, goals should be adjusted and updated periodically, so be flexible and get excited about finally creating the future you've always dreamed of!

*"The greater danger is not that your hopes are too high and you fail to reach them; it's that they're too low and you do."*

—Michelangelo

**Goal 1)** _____

  **Why:** _____

_____

**Goal 2)** _____

  **Why:** _____

_____

**Goal 3)** _____

  **Why:** _____

_____

**Goal 4)** _____

  **Why:** _____

_____

**Goal 5)** _____

  **Why:** _____

_____

**The Benefits of Super Immunity:**

- Powerful protection from cancers
- Rarely get colds or flu
- Protection from bacterial and viral infections
- An eating style that protects against the most common chronic diseases, such as heart disease and diabetes

**The Most important things to remember about eating for Super Immunity**

1. _____
2. _____
3. _____
4. _____
5. _____

## YOUR WEEKLY SHOPPING LIST

1. _____
2. _____
3. _____
4. _____
5. _____
6. _____
7. _____
8. _____
9. _____
10. _____
11. _____
12. _____
13. _____
14. _____
15. _____

16. _____
17. _____
18. _____
19. _____
20. _____
21. _____
22. _____
23. _____
24. _____
25. _____
26. _____
27. _____
28. _____
29. _____
30. _____

31. _____
32. _____
33. _____
34. _____
35. _____
36. _____
37. _____
38. _____
39. _____
40. _____
41. _____
42. _____
43. _____
44. _____
45. _____

## 3-DAY MEAL PLANNING

**DAY 1**

BREAKFAST

LUNCH

DINNER

**DAY 2**

BREAKFAST

LUNCH

DINNER

**DAY 3**

BREAKFAST

LUNCH

DINNER

## RECIPE PLANNING

### SALADS AND SALAD DRESSINGS

INGREDIENTS

PREPARATION INSTRUCTIONS

### SOUPS/STEWS

INGREDIENTS

PREPARATION INSTRUCTIONS

## VEGETABLE-BASED MAIN DISH

| INGREDIENTS | PREPARATION INSTRUCTIONS |
|---|---|
| | |

## SMOOTHIES

| INGREDIENTS | PREPARATION INSTRUCTIONS |
|---|---|
| | |

## SORBETS AND DESSERTS

| INGREDIENTS | PREPARATION INSTRUCTIONS |
| --- | --- |
| | |

**Acceptable prepared foods**

1. _____

2. _____

3. _____

4. _____

5. _____

**Strategies for eating in restaurants**

**DOs**

1. _____

2. _____

3. _____

4. _____

5. _____

**DON'Ts**

1. _____

2. _____

3. _____

4. _____

5. _____

## WEEKLY PLANNER

Use this page to plan out when you will complete the following activities each week:

**SHOP**          **COOK**          **EAT LEFTOVERS**          **EXERCISE**

|           | MORNING | AFTERNOON | EVENING |
|-----------|---------|-----------|---------|
| **Monday**    |         |           |         |
| **Tuesday**   |         |           |         |
| **Wednesday** |         |           |         |
| **Thursday**  |         |           |         |
| **Friday**    |         |           |         |
| **Saturday**  |         |           |         |
| **Sunday**    |         |           |         |

## HOW TO USE THE CALENDAR SECTION OF THIS BOOK

1. The grid lists categories for foods, supplements, and exercise.

2. Select your set of Dietary Goals.
   (Prevention, Autoimmune, or Cancer; pp. 27-31)

3. Each day, put a check mark next to each goal that you met that day.

4. Add up the number of check marks at the end of each week to get your Super Immunity score.

**Watch your score improve over time, as you learn how to live a nutritarian lifestyle!**

## WEEKLY CALENDAR

**DID I MEET EACH OF MY GOALS TODAY?**

| | MON | TUE | WED | THU | FRI | SAT | SUN | MY WEEKLY SUPER IMMUNITY SCORE |
|---|---|---|---|---|---|---|---|---|
| **GREENS** (and other vegetables) | | | | | | | | |
| Raw leafy greens | | | | | | | | |
| Other raw vegetables | | | | | | | | |
| Total cooked vegetables | | | | | | | | |
| Cruciferous vegetables | | | | | | | | |
| Fresh vegetable juice | | | | | | | | |
| **BEANS** | | | | | | | | |
| Total beans and lentils | | | | | | | | |
| **ONIONS** | | | | | | | | |
| Vegetables from the onion family | | | | | | | | |
| **MUSHROOMS** | | | | | | | | |
| Cooked mushrooms | | | | | | | | |
| **BERRIES** (and other fruit) | | | | | | | | |
| Berries/pomegranate | | | | | | | | |
| Other fruit | | | | | | | | |
| Dried fruit | | | | | | | | |
| **NUTS AND SEEDS** | | | | | | | | |
| High omega-3: walnuts, chia, hemp, flax | | | | | | | | |
| Other nuts and seeds, avocado | | | | | | | | |
| **LIMITED FOODS** | | | | | | | | |
| Whole grains/starchy vegetables | | | | | | | | |
| Poultry, eggs, dairy, and fish | | | | | | | | |
| Oils | | | | | | | | |
| White potatoes | | | | | | | | |
| Added sodium | | | | | | | | |
| **FOODS TO AVOID** | | | | | | | | |
| Red meats | | | | | | | | |
| Sugar and sweets | | | | | | | | |
| White rice, white flour products, and processed foods | | | | | | | | |
| **SUPPLEMENTS** — *Which supplements did I take today?* | | | | | | | | |
| Multivitamin (no vitamins A or E, beta-carotene, folic acid, copper) | | | | | | | | |
| Vitamin D | | | | | | | | |
| Omega-3 fatty acids | | | | | | | | |
| Other | | | | | | | | |
| **EXERCISE** — *How much did I exercise today?* | | | | | | | | |
| Easy to moderate activity | | | | | | | | |
| Vigorous activity | | | | | | | | |

**TOTAL SCORE:**

# WEEKLY CALENDAR

**DID I MEET EACH OF MY GOALS TODAY?**

| | MON | TUE | WED | THU | FRI | SAT | SUN | MY WEEKLY SUPER IMMUNITY SCORE |
|---|---|---|---|---|---|---|---|---|
| **GREENS** (and other vegetables) | | | | | | | | |
| Raw leafy greens | | | | | | | | |
| Other raw vegetables | | | | | | | | |
| Total cooked vegetables | | | | | | | | |
| Cruciferous vegetables | | | | | | | | |
| Fresh vegetable juice | | | | | | | | |
| **BEANS** | | | | | | | | |
| Total beans and lentils | | | | | | | | |
| **ONIONS** | | | | | | | | |
| Vegetables from the onion family | | | | | | | | |
| **MUSHROOMS** | | | | | | | | |
| Cooked mushrooms | | | | | | | | |
| **BERRIES** (and other fruit) | | | | | | | | |
| Berries/pomegranate | | | | | | | | |
| Other fruit | | | | | | | | |
| Dried fruit | | | | | | | | |
| **NUTS AND SEEDS** | | | | | | | | |
| High omega-3: walnuts, chia, hemp, flax | | | | | | | | |
| Other nuts and seeds, avocado | | | | | | | | |
| **LIMITED FOODS** | | | | | | | | |
| Whole grains/starchy vegetables | | | | | | | | |
| Poultry, eggs, dairy, and fish | | | | | | | | |
| Oils | | | | | | | | |
| White potatoes | | | | | | | | |
| Added sodium | | | | | | | | |
| **FOODS TO AVOID** | | | | | | | | |
| Red meats | | | | | | | | |
| Sugar and sweets | | | | | | | | |
| White rice, white flour products, and processed foods | | | | | | | | |
| **SUPPLEMENTS — Which supplements did I take today?** | | | | | | | | |
| Multivitamin (no vitamins A or E, beta-carotene, folic acid, copper) | | | | | | | | |
| Vitamin D | | | | | | | | |
| Omega-3 fatty acids | | | | | | | | |
| Other | | | | | | | | |
| **EXERCISE — How much did I exercise today?** | | | | | | | | |
| Easy to moderate activity | | | | | | | | |
| Vigorous activity | | | | | | | | |

**TOTAL SCORE:**

## DID I MEET EACH OF MY GOALS TODAY?

| | MON | TUE | WED | THU | FRI | SAT | SUN | MY WEEKLY SUPER IMMUNITY SCORE |
|---|---|---|---|---|---|---|---|---|
| **GREENS** (*and other vegetables*) | | | | | | | | |
| Raw leafy greens | | | | | | | | |
| Other raw vegetables | | | | | | | | |
| Total cooked vegetables | | | | | | | | |
| Cruciferous vegetables | | | | | | | | |
| Fresh vegetable juice | | | | | | | | |
| **BEANS** | | | | | | | | |
| Total beans and lentils | | | | | | | | |
| **ONIONS** | | | | | | | | |
| Vegetables from the onion family | | | | | | | | |
| **MUSHROOMS** | | | | | | | | |
| Cooked mushrooms | | | | | | | | |
| **BERRIES** (*and other fruit*) | | | | | | | | |
| Berries/pomegranate | | | | | | | | |
| Other fruit | | | | | | | | |
| Dried fruit | | | | | | | | |
| **NUTS AND SEEDS** | | | | | | | | |
| High omega-3: walnuts, chia, hemp, flax | | | | | | | | |
| Other nuts and seeds, avocado | | | | | | | | |
| **LIMITED FOODS** | | | | | | | | |
| Whole grains/starchy vegetables | | | | | | | | |
| Poultry, eggs, dairy, and fish | | | | | | | | |
| Oils | | | | | | | | |
| White potatoes | | | | | | | | |
| Added sodium | | | | | | | | |
| **FOODS TO AVOID** | | | | | | | | |
| Red meats | | | | | | | | |
| Sugar and sweets | | | | | | | | |
| White rice, white flour products, and processed foods | | | | | | | | |
| **SUPPLEMENTS — *Which supplements did I take today?*** | | | | | | | | |
| Multivitamin (no vitamins A or E, beta-carotene, folic acid, copper) | | | | | | | | |
| Vitamin D | | | | | | | | |
| Omega-3 fatty acids | | | | | | | | |
| Other | | | | | | | | |
| **EXERCISE — *How much did I exercise today?*** | | | | | | | | |
| Easy to moderate activity | | | | | | | | |
| Vigorous activity | | | | | | | | |

**TOTAL SCORE:**

# WEEKLY CALENDAR

**DID I MEET EACH OF MY GOALS TODAY?**

| | MON | TUE | WED | THU | FRI | SAT | SUN | MY WEEKLY SUPER IMMUNITY SCORE |
|---|---|---|---|---|---|---|---|---|
| **GREENS** (and other vegetables) | | | | | | | | |
| Raw leafy greens | | | | | | | | |
| Other raw vegetables | | | | | | | | |
| Total cooked vegetables | | | | | | | | |
| Cruciferous vegetables | | | | | | | | |
| Fresh vegetable juice | | | | | | | | |
| **BEANS** | | | | | | | | |
| Total beans and lentils | | | | | | | | |
| **ONIONS** | | | | | | | | |
| Vegetables from the onion family | | | | | | | | |
| **MUSHROOMS** | | | | | | | | |
| Cooked mushrooms | | | | | | | | |
| **BERRIES** (and other fruit) | | | | | | | | |
| Berries/pomegranate | | | | | | | | |
| Other fruit | | | | | | | | |
| Dried fruit | | | | | | | | |
| **NUTS AND SEEDS** | | | | | | | | |
| High omega-3: walnuts, chia, hemp, flax | | | | | | | | |
| Other nuts and seeds, avocado | | | | | | | | |
| **LIMITED FOODS** | | | | | | | | |
| Whole grains/starchy vegetables | | | | | | | | |
| Poultry, eggs, dairy, and fish | | | | | | | | |
| Oils | | | | | | | | |
| White potatoes | | | | | | | | |
| Added sodium | | | | | | | | |
| **FOODS TO AVOID** | | | | | | | | |
| Red meats | | | | | | | | |
| Sugar and sweets | | | | | | | | |
| White rice, white flour products, and processed foods | | | | | | | | |
| **SUPPLEMENTS — *Which supplements did I take today?*** | | | | | | | | |
| Multivitamin (no vitamins A or E, beta-carotene, folic acid, copper) | | | | | | | | |
| Vitamin D | | | | | | | | |
| Omega-3 fatty acids | | | | | | | | |
| Other | | | | | | | | |
| **EXERCISE — *How much did I exercise today?*** | | | | | | | | |
| Easy to moderate activity | | | | | | | | |
| Vigorous activity | | | | | | | | |

**TOTAL SCORE:**

**DID I MEET EACH OF MY GOALS TODAY?**

| | MON | TUE | WED | THU | FRI | SAT | SUN | MY WEEKLY SUPER IMMUNITY SCORE |
|---|---|---|---|---|---|---|---|---|
| **GREENS** *(and other vegetables)* | | | | | | | | |
| Raw leafy greens | | | | | | | | |
| Other raw vegetables | | | | | | | | |
| Total cooked vegetables | | | | | | | | |
| Cruciferous vegetables | | | | | | | | |
| Fresh vegetable juice | | | | | | | | |
| **BEANS** | | | | | | | | |
| Total beans and lentils | | | | | | | | |
| **ONIONS** | | | | | | | | |
| Vegetables from the onion family | | | | | | | | |
| **MUSHROOMS** | | | | | | | | |
| Cooked mushrooms | | | | | | | | |
| **BERRIES** *(and other fruit)* | | | | | | | | |
| Berries/pomegranate | | | | | | | | |
| Other fruit | | | | | | | | |
| Dried fruit | | | | | | | | |
| **NUTS AND SEEDS** | | | | | | | | |
| High omega-3: walnuts, chia, hemp, flax | | | | | | | | |
| Other nuts and seeds, avocado | | | | | | | | |
| **LIMITED FOODS** | | | | | | | | |
| Whole grains/starchy vegetables | | | | | | | | |
| Poultry, eggs, dairy, and fish | | | | | | | | |
| Oils | | | | | | | | |
| White potatoes | | | | | | | | |
| Added sodium | | | | | | | | |
| **FOODS TO AVOID** | | | | | | | | |
| Red meats | | | | | | | | |
| Sugar and sweets | | | | | | | | |
| White rice, white flour products, and processed foods | | | | | | | | |
| **SUPPLEMENTS — *Which supplements did I take today?*** | | | | | | | | |
| Multivitamin (no vitamins A or E, beta-carotene, folic acid, copper) | | | | | | | | |
| Vitamin D | | | | | | | | |
| Omega-3 fatty acids | | | | | | | | |
| Other | | | | | | | | |
| **EXERCISE — *How much did I exercise today?*** | | | | | | | | |
| Easy to moderate activity | | | | | | | | |
| Vigorous activity | | | | | | | | |

**TOTAL SCORE:**

# WEEKLY CALENDAR

## DID I MEET EACH OF MY GOALS TODAY?

| | MON | TUE | WED | THU | FRI | SAT | SUN | MY WEEKLY SUPER IMMUNITY SCORE |
|---|---|---|---|---|---|---|---|---|
| **GREENS** *(and other vegetables)* | | | | | | | | |
| Raw leafy greens | | | | | | | | |
| Other raw vegetables | | | | | | | | |
| Total cooked vegetables | | | | | | | | |
| Cruciferous vegetables | | | | | | | | |
| Fresh vegetable juice | | | | | | | | |
| **BEANS** | | | | | | | | |
| Total beans and lentils | | | | | | | | |
| **ONIONS** | | | | | | | | |
| Vegetables from the onion family | | | | | | | | |
| **MUSHROOMS** | | | | | | | | |
| Cooked mushrooms | | | | | | | | |
| **BERRIES** *(and other fruit)* | | | | | | | | |
| Berries/pomegranate | | | | | | | | |
| Other fruit | | | | | | | | |
| Dried fruit | | | | | | | | |
| **NUTS AND SEEDS** | | | | | | | | |
| High omega-3: walnuts, chia, hemp, flax | | | | | | | | |
| Other nuts and seeds, avocado | | | | | | | | |
| **LIMITED FOODS** | | | | | | | | |
| Whole grains/starchy vegetables | | | | | | | | |
| Poultry, eggs, dairy, and fish | | | | | | | | |
| Oils | | | | | | | | |
| White potatoes | | | | | | | | |
| Added sodium | | | | | | | | |
| **FOODS TO AVOID** | | | | | | | | |
| Red meats | | | | | | | | |
| Sugar and sweets | | | | | | | | |
| White rice, white flour products, and processed foods | | | | | | | | |
| **SUPPLEMENTS — *Which supplements did I take today?*** | | | | | | | | |
| Multivitamin (no vitamins A or E, beta-carotene, folic acid, copper) | | | | | | | | |
| Vitamin D | | | | | | | | |
| Omega-3 fatty acids | | | | | | | | |
| Other | | | | | | | | |
| **EXERCISE — *How much did I exercise today?*** | | | | | | | | |
| Easy to moderate activity | | | | | | | | |
| Vigorous activity | | | | | | | | |

**TOTAL SCORE:**

## WEEKLY CALENDAR

**DID I MEET EACH OF MY GOALS TODAY?**

| | MON | TUE | WED | THU | FRI | SAT | SUN | MY WEEKLY SUPER IMMUNITY SCORE |
|---|---|---|---|---|---|---|---|---|
| **GREENS** (*and other vegetables*) | | | | | | | | |
| Raw leafy greens | | | | | | | | |
| Other raw vegetables | | | | | | | | |
| Total cooked vegetables | | | | | | | | |
| Cruciferous vegetables | | | | | | | | |
| Fresh vegetable juice | | | | | | | | |
| **BEANS** | | | | | | | | |
| Total beans and lentils | | | | | | | | |
| **ONIONS** | | | | | | | | |
| Vegetables from the onion family | | | | | | | | |
| **MUSHROOMS** | | | | | | | | |
| Cooked mushrooms | | | | | | | | |
| **BERRIES** (*and other fruit*) | | | | | | | | |
| Berries/pomegranate | | | | | | | | |
| Other fruit | | | | | | | | |
| Dried fruit | | | | | | | | |
| **NUTS AND SEEDS** | | | | | | | | |
| High omega-3: walnuts, chia, hemp, flax | | | | | | | | |
| Other nuts and seeds, avocado | | | | | | | | |
| **LIMITED FOODS** | | | | | | | | |
| Whole grains/starchy vegetables | | | | | | | | |
| Poultry, eggs, dairy, and fish | | | | | | | | |
| Oils | | | | | | | | |
| White potatoes | | | | | | | | |
| Added sodium | | | | | | | | |
| **FOODS TO AVOID** | | | | | | | | |
| Red meats | | | | | | | | |
| Sugar and sweets | | | | | | | | |
| White rice, white flour products, and processed foods | | | | | | | | |
| **SUPPLEMENTS** — *Which supplements did I take today?* | | | | | | | | |
| Multivitamin (no vitamins A or E, beta-carotene, folic acid, copper) | | | | | | | | |
| Vitamin D | | | | | | | | |
| Omega-3 fatty acids | | | | | | | | |
| Other | | | | | | | | |
| **EXERCISE** — *How much did I exercise today?* | | | | | | | | |
| Easy to moderate activity | | | | | | | | |
| Vigorous activity | | | | | | | | |

**TOTAL SCORE:**

# WEEKLY CALENDAR

## DID I MEET EACH OF MY GOALS TODAY?

| | MON | TUE | WED | THU | FRI | SAT | SUN | MY WEEKLY SUPER IMMUNITY SCORE |
|---|---|---|---|---|---|---|---|---|
| **GREENS** (and other vegetables) | | | | | | | | |
| Raw leafy greens | | | | | | | | |
| Other raw vegetables | | | | | | | | |
| Total cooked vegetables | | | | | | | | |
| Cruciferous vegetables | | | | | | | | |
| Fresh vegetable juice | | | | | | | | |
| **BEANS** | | | | | | | | |
| Total beans and lentils | | | | | | | | |
| **ONIONS** | | | | | | | | |
| Vegetables from the onion family | | | | | | | | |
| **MUSHROOMS** | | | | | | | | |
| Cooked mushrooms | | | | | | | | |
| **BERRIES** (and other fruit) | | | | | | | | |
| Berries/pomegranate | | | | | | | | |
| Other fruit | | | | | | | | |
| Dried fruit | | | | | | | | |
| **NUTS AND SEEDS** | | | | | | | | |
| High omega-3: walnuts, chia, hemp, flax | | | | | | | | |
| Other nuts and seeds, avocado | | | | | | | | |
| **LIMITED FOODS** | | | | | | | | |
| Whole grains/starchy vegetables | | | | | | | | |
| Poultry, eggs, dairy, and fish | | | | | | | | |
| Oils | | | | | | | | |
| White potatoes | | | | | | | | |
| Added sodium | | | | | | | | |
| **FOODS TO AVOID** | | | | | | | | |
| Red meats | | | | | | | | |
| Sugar and sweets | | | | | | | | |
| White rice, white flour products, and processed foods | | | | | | | | |
| **SUPPLEMENTS — Which supplements did I take today?** | | | | | | | | |
| Multivitamin (no vitamins A or E, beta-carotene, folic acid, copper) | | | | | | | | |
| Vitamin D | | | | | | | | |
| Omega-3 fatty acids | | | | | | | | |
| Other | | | | | | | | |
| **EXERCISE — How much did I exercise today?** | | | | | | | | |
| Easy to moderate activity | | | | | | | | |
| Vigorous activity | | | | | | | | |

**TOTAL SCORE:**

## WEEKLY CALENDAR

### DID I MEET EACH OF MY GOALS TODAY?

| | MON | TUE | WED | THU | FRI | SAT | SUN | MY WEEKLY SUPER IMMUNITY SCORE |
|---|---|---|---|---|---|---|---|---|
| **GREENS** (and other vegetables) | | | | | | | | |
| Raw leafy greens | | | | | | | | |
| Other raw vegetables | | | | | | | | |
| Total cooked vegetables | | | | | | | | |
| Cruciferous vegetables | | | | | | | | |
| Fresh vegetable juice | | | | | | | | |
| **BEANS** | | | | | | | | |
| Total beans and lentils | | | | | | | | |
| **ONIONS** | | | | | | | | |
| Vegetables from the onion family | | | | | | | | |
| **MUSHROOMS** | | | | | | | | |
| Cooked mushrooms | | | | | | | | |
| **BERRIES** (and other fruit) | | | | | | | | |
| Berries/pomegranate | | | | | | | | |
| Other fruit | | | | | | | | |
| Dried fruit | | | | | | | | |
| **NUTS AND SEEDS** | | | | | | | | |
| High omega-3: walnuts, chia, hemp, flax | | | | | | | | |
| Other nuts and seeds, avocado | | | | | | | | |
| **LIMITED FOODS** | | | | | | | | |
| Whole grains/starchy vegetables | | | | | | | | |
| Poultry, eggs, dairy, and fish | | | | | | | | |
| Oils | | | | | | | | |
| White potatoes | | | | | | | | |
| Added sodium | | | | | | | | |
| **FOODS TO AVOID** | | | | | | | | |
| Red meats | | | | | | | | |
| Sugar and sweets | | | | | | | | |
| White rice, white flour products, and processed foods | | | | | | | | |
| **SUPPLEMENTS — Which supplements did I take today?** | | | | | | | | |
| Multivitamin (no vitamins A or E, beta-carotene, folic acid, copper) | | | | | | | | |
| Vitamin D | | | | | | | | |
| Omega-3 fatty acids | | | | | | | | |
| Other | | | | | | | | |
| **EXERCISE — How much did I exercise today?** | | | | | | | | |
| Easy to moderate activity | | | | | | | | |
| Vigorous activity | | | | | | | | |

**TOTAL SCORE:**

# WEEKLY CALENDAR

## DID I MEET EACH OF MY GOALS TODAY?

| | MON | TUE | WED | THU | FRI | SAT | SUN | MY WEEKLY SUPER IMMUNITY SCORE |
|---|---|---|---|---|---|---|---|---|
| **GREENS** (and other vegetables) | | | | | | | | |
| Raw leafy greens | | | | | | | | |
| Other raw vegetables | | | | | | | | |
| Total cooked vegetables | | | | | | | | |
| Cruciferous vegetables | | | | | | | | |
| Fresh vegetable juice | | | | | | | | |
| **BEANS** | | | | | | | | |
| Total beans and lentils | | | | | | | | |
| **ONIONS** | | | | | | | | |
| Vegetables from the onion family | | | | | | | | |
| **MUSHROOMS** | | | | | | | | |
| Cooked mushrooms | | | | | | | | |
| **BERRIES** (and other fruit) | | | | | | | | |
| Berries/pomegranate | | | | | | | | |
| Other fruit | | | | | | | | |
| Dried fruit | | | | | | | | |
| **NUTS AND SEEDS** | | | | | | | | |
| High omega-3: walnuts, chia, hemp, flax | | | | | | | | |
| Other nuts and seeds, avocado | | | | | | | | |
| **LIMITED FOODS** | | | | | | | | |
| Whole grains/starchy vegetables | | | | | | | | |
| Poultry, eggs, dairy, and fish | | | | | | | | |
| Oils | | | | | | | | |
| White potatoes | | | | | | | | |
| Added sodium | | | | | | | | |
| **FOODS TO AVOID** | | | | | | | | |
| Red meats | | | | | | | | |
| Sugar and sweets | | | | | | | | |
| White rice, white flour products, and processed foods | | | | | | | | |
| **SUPPLEMENTS — Which supplements did I take today?** | | | | | | | | |
| Multivitamin (no vitamins A or E, beta-carotene, folic acid, copper) | | | | | | | | |
| Vitamin D | | | | | | | | |
| Omega-3 fatty acids | | | | | | | | |
| Other | | | | | | | | |
| **EXERCISE — How much did I exercise today?** | | | | | | | | |
| Easy to moderate activity | | | | | | | | |
| Vigorous activity | | | | | | | | |

**TOTAL SCORE:**

## WEEKLY CALENDAR

**DID I MEET EACH OF MY GOALS TODAY?**

| | MON | TUE | WED | THU | FRI | SAT | SUN | MY WEEKLY SUPER IMMUNITY SCORE |
|---|---|---|---|---|---|---|---|---|
| **GREENS** (and other vegetables) | | | | | | | | |
| Raw leafy greens | | | | | | | | |
| Other raw vegetables | | | | | | | | |
| Total cooked vegetables | | | | | | | | |
| Cruciferous vegetables | | | | | | | | |
| Fresh vegetable juice | | | | | | | | |
| **BEANS** | | | | | | | | |
| Total beans and lentils | | | | | | | | |
| **ONIONS** | | | | | | | | |
| Vegetables from the onion family | | | | | | | | |
| **MUSHROOMS** | | | | | | | | |
| Cooked mushrooms | | | | | | | | |
| **BERRIES** (and other fruit) | | | | | | | | |
| Berries/pomegranate | | | | | | | | |
| Other fruit | | | | | | | | |
| Dried fruit | | | | | | | | |
| **NUTS AND SEEDS** | | | | | | | | |
| High omega-3: walnuts, chia, hemp, flax | | | | | | | | |
| Other nuts and seeds, avocado | | | | | | | | |
| **LIMITED FOODS** | | | | | | | | |
| Whole grains/starchy vegetables | | | | | | | | |
| Poultry, eggs, dairy, and fish | | | | | | | | |
| Oils | | | | | | | | |
| White potatoes | | | | | | | | |
| Added sodium | | | | | | | | |
| **FOODS TO AVOID** | | | | | | | | |
| Red meats | | | | | | | | |
| Sugar and sweets | | | | | | | | |
| White rice, white flour products, and processed foods | | | | | | | | |
| **SUPPLEMENTS** — *Which supplements did I take today?* | | | | | | | | |
| Multivitamin (no vitamins A or E, beta-carotene, folic acid, copper) | | | | | | | | |
| Vitamin D | | | | | | | | |
| Omega-3 fatty acids | | | | | | | | |
| Other | | | | | | | | |
| **EXERCISE** — *How much did I exercise today?* | | | | | | | | |
| Easy to moderate activity | | | | | | | | |
| Vigorous activity | | | | | | | | |

**TOTAL SCORE:**

## WEEKLY CALENDAR

**DID I MEET EACH OF MY GOALS TODAY?**

| | MON | TUE | WED | THU | FRI | SAT | SUN | MY WEEKLY SUPER IMMUNITY SCORE |
|---|---|---|---|---|---|---|---|---|
| **GREENS** *(and other vegetables)* | | | | | | | | |
| Raw leafy greens | | | | | | | | |
| Other raw vegetables | | | | | | | | |
| Total cooked vegetables | | | | | | | | |
| Cruciferous vegetables | | | | | | | | |
| Fresh vegetable juice | | | | | | | | |
| **BEANS** | | | | | | | | |
| Total beans and lentils | | | | | | | | |
| **ONIONS** | | | | | | | | |
| Vegetables from the onion family | | | | | | | | |
| **MUSHROOMS** | | | | | | | | |
| Cooked mushrooms | | | | | | | | |
| **BERRIES** *(and other fruit)* | | | | | | | | |
| Berries/pomegranate | | | | | | | | |
| Other fruit | | | | | | | | |
| Dried fruit | | | | | | | | |
| **NUTS AND SEEDS** | | | | | | | | |
| High omega-3: walnuts, chia, hemp, flax | | | | | | | | |
| Other nuts and seeds, avocado | | | | | | | | |
| **LIMITED FOODS** | | | | | | | | |
| Whole grains/starchy vegetables | | | | | | | | |
| Poultry, eggs, dairy, and fish | | | | | | | | |
| Oils | | | | | | | | |
| White potatoes | | | | | | | | |
| Added sodium | | | | | | | | |
| **FOODS TO AVOID** | | | | | | | | |
| Red meats | | | | | | | | |
| Sugar and sweets | | | | | | | | |
| White rice, white flour products, and processed foods | | | | | | | | |
| **SUPPLEMENTS — *Which supplements did I take today?*** | | | | | | | | |
| Multivitamin (no vitamins A or E, beta-carotene, folic acid, copper) | | | | | | | | |
| Vitamin D | | | | | | | | |
| Omega-3 fatty acids | | | | | | | | |
| Other | | | | | | | | |
| **EXERCISE — *How much did I exercise today?*** | | | | | | | | |
| Easy to moderate activity | | | | | | | | |
| Vigorous activity | | | | | | | | |

**TOTAL SCORE:**

## WEEKLY CALENDAR

**DID I MEET EACH OF MY GOALS TODAY?**

| | MON | TUE | WED | THU | FRI | SAT | SUN | MY WEEKLY SUPER IMMUNITY SCORE |
|---|---|---|---|---|---|---|---|---|
| **GREENS** (and other vegetables) | | | | | | | | |
| Raw leafy greens | | | | | | | | |
| Other raw vegetables | | | | | | | | |
| Total cooked vegetables | | | | | | | | |
| Cruciferous vegetables | | | | | | | | |
| Fresh vegetable juice | | | | | | | | |
| **BEANS** | | | | | | | | |
| Total beans and lentils | | | | | | | | |
| **ONIONS** | | | | | | | | |
| Vegetables from the onion family | | | | | | | | |
| **MUSHROOMS** | | | | | | | | |
| Cooked mushrooms | | | | | | | | |
| **BERRIES** (and other fruit) | | | | | | | | |
| Berries/pomegranate | | | | | | | | |
| Other fruit | | | | | | | | |
| Dried fruit | | | | | | | | |
| **NUTS AND SEEDS** | | | | | | | | |
| High omega-3: walnuts, chia, hemp, flax | | | | | | | | |
| Other nuts and seeds, avocado | | | | | | | | |
| **LIMITED FOODS** | | | | | | | | |
| Whole grains/starchy vegetables | | | | | | | | |
| Poultry, eggs, dairy, and fish | | | | | | | | |
| Oils | | | | | | | | |
| White potatoes | | | | | | | | |
| Added sodium | | | | | | | | |
| **FOODS TO AVOID** | | | | | | | | |
| Red meats | | | | | | | | |
| Sugar and sweets | | | | | | | | |
| White rice, white flour products, and processed foods | | | | | | | | |
| **SUPPLEMENTS — Which supplements did I take today?** | | | | | | | | |
| Multivitamin (no vitamins A or E, beta-carotene, folic acid, copper) | | | | | | | | |
| Vitamin D | | | | | | | | |
| Omega-3 fatty acids | | | | | | | | |
| Other | | | | | | | | |
| **EXERCISE — How much did I exercise today?** | | | | | | | | |
| Easy to moderate activity | | | | | | | | |
| Vigorous activity | | | | | | | | |

**TOTAL SCORE:**

# WEEKLY CALENDAR

**DID I MEET EACH OF MY GOALS TODAY?**

| | MON | TUE | WED | THU | FRI | SAT | SUN | MY WEEKLY SUPER IMMUNITY SCORE |
|---|---|---|---|---|---|---|---|---|
| **GREENS** *(and other vegetables)* | | | | | | | | |
| Raw leafy greens | | | | | | | | |
| Other raw vegetables | | | | | | | | |
| Total cooked vegetables | | | | | | | | |
| Cruciferous vegetables | | | | | | | | |
| Fresh vegetable juice | | | | | | | | |
| **BEANS** | | | | | | | | |
| Total beans and lentils | | | | | | | | |
| **ONIONS** | | | | | | | | |
| Vegetables from the onion family | | | | | | | | |
| **MUSHROOMS** | | | | | | | | |
| Cooked mushrooms | | | | | | | | |
| **BERRIES** *(and other fruit)* | | | | | | | | |
| Berries/pomegranate | | | | | | | | |
| Other fruit | | | | | | | | |
| Dried fruit | | | | | | | | |
| **NUTS AND SEEDS** | | | | | | | | |
| High omega-3: walnuts, chia, hemp, flax | | | | | | | | |
| Other nuts and seeds, avocado | | | | | | | | |
| **LIMITED FOODS** | | | | | | | | |
| Whole grains/starchy vegetables | | | | | | | | |
| Poultry, eggs, dairy, and fish | | | | | | | | |
| Oils | | | | | | | | |
| White potatoes | | | | | | | | |
| Added sodium | | | | | | | | |
| **FOODS TO AVOID** | | | | | | | | |
| Red meats | | | | | | | | |
| Sugar and sweets | | | | | | | | |
| White rice, white flour products, and processed foods | | | | | | | | |
| **SUPPLEMENTS — *Which supplements did I take today?*** | | | | | | | | |
| Multivitamin (no vitamins A or E, beta-carotene, folic acid, copper) | | | | | | | | |
| Vitamin D | | | | | | | | |
| Omega-3 fatty acids | | | | | | | | |
| Other | | | | | | | | |
| **EXERCISE — *How much did I exercise today?*** | | | | | | | | |
| Easy to moderate activity | | | | | | | | |
| Vigorous activity | | | | | | | | |

**TOTAL SCORE:** [          ]

## WEEKLY CALENDAR

**DID I MEET EACH OF MY GOALS TODAY?**

| | MON | TUE | WED | THU | FRI | SAT | SUN | MY WEEKLY SUPER IMMUNITY SCORE |
|---|---|---|---|---|---|---|---|---|
| **GREENS** *(and other vegetables)* | | | | | | | | |
| Raw leafy greens | | | | | | | | |
| Other raw vegetables | | | | | | | | |
| Total cooked vegetables | | | | | | | | |
| Cruciferous vegetables | | | | | | | | |
| Fresh vegetable juice | | | | | | | | |
| **BEANS** | | | | | | | | |
| Total beans and lentils | | | | | | | | |
| **ONIONS** | | | | | | | | |
| Vegetables from the onion family | | | | | | | | |
| **MUSHROOMS** | | | | | | | | |
| Cooked mushrooms | | | | | | | | |
| **BERRIES** *(and other fruit)* | | | | | | | | |
| Berries/pomegranate | | | | | | | | |
| Other fruit | | | | | | | | |
| Dried fruit | | | | | | | | |
| **NUTS AND SEEDS** | | | | | | | | |
| High omega-3: walnuts, chia, hemp, flax | | | | | | | | |
| Other nuts and seeds, avocado | | | | | | | | |
| **LIMITED FOODS** | | | | | | | | |
| Whole grains/starchy vegetables | | | | | | | | |
| Poultry, eggs, dairy, and fish | | | | | | | | |
| Oils | | | | | | | | |
| White potatoes | | | | | | | | |
| Added sodium | | | | | | | | |
| **FOODS TO AVOID** | | | | | | | | |
| Red meats | | | | | | | | |
| Sugar and sweets | | | | | | | | |
| White rice, white flour products, and processed foods | | | | | | | | |
| **SUPPLEMENTS — *Which supplements did I take today?*** | | | | | | | | |
| Multivitamin (no vitamins A or E, beta-carotene, folic acid, copper) | | | | | | | | |
| Vitamin D | | | | | | | | |
| Omega-3 fatty acids | | | | | | | | |
| Other | | | | | | | | |
| **EXERCISE — *How much did I exercise today?*** | | | | | | | | |
| Easy to moderate activity | | | | | | | | |
| Vigorous activity | | | | | | | | |

**TOTAL SCORE:**

## WEEKLY CALENDAR

**DID I MEET EACH OF MY GOALS TODAY?**

| | MON | TUE | WED | THU | FRI | SAT | SUN | MY WEEKLY SUPER IMMUNITY SCORE |
|---|---|---|---|---|---|---|---|---|
| **GREENS** (*and other vegetables*) | | | | | | | | |
| Raw leafy greens | | | | | | | | |
| Other raw vegetables | | | | | | | | |
| Total cooked vegetables | | | | | | | | |
| Cruciferous vegetables | | | | | | | | |
| Fresh vegetable juice | | | | | | | | |
| **BEANS** | | | | | | | | |
| Total beans and lentils | | | | | | | | |
| **ONIONS** | | | | | | | | |
| Vegetables from the onion family | | | | | | | | |
| **MUSHROOMS** | | | | | | | | |
| Cooked mushrooms | | | | | | | | |
| **BERRIES** (*and other fruit*) | | | | | | | | |
| Berries/pomegranate | | | | | | | | |
| Other fruit | | | | | | | | |
| Dried fruit | | | | | | | | |
| **NUTS AND SEEDS** | | | | | | | | |
| High omega-3: walnuts, chia, hemp, flax | | | | | | | | |
| Other nuts and seeds, avocado | | | | | | | | |
| **LIMITED FOODS** | | | | | | | | |
| Whole grains/starchy vegetables | | | | | | | | |
| Poultry, eggs, dairy, and fish | | | | | | | | |
| Oils | | | | | | | | |
| White potatoes | | | | | | | | |
| Added sodium | | | | | | | | |
| **FOODS TO AVOID** | | | | | | | | |
| Red meats | | | | | | | | |
| Sugar and sweets | | | | | | | | |
| White rice, white flour products, and processed foods | | | | | | | | |
| **SUPPLEMENTS** — *Which supplements did I take today?* | | | | | | | | |
| Multivitamin (no vitamins A or E, beta-carotene, folic acid, copper) | | | | | | | | |
| Vitamin D | | | | | | | | |
| Omega-3 fatty acids | | | | | | | | |
| Other | | | | | | | | |
| **EXERCISE** — *How much did I exercise today?* | | | | | | | | |
| Easy to moderate activity | | | | | | | | |
| Vigorous activity | | | | | | | | |

**TOTAL SCORE:**

## WEEKLY CALENDAR

**DID I MEET EACH OF MY GOALS TODAY?**

| | MON | TUE | WED | THU | FRI | SAT | SUN | MY WEEKLY SUPER IMMUNITY SCORE |
|---|---|---|---|---|---|---|---|---|
| **GREENS** *(and other vegetables)* | | | | | | | | |
| Raw leafy greens | | | | | | | | |
| Other raw vegetables | | | | | | | | |
| Total cooked vegetables | | | | | | | | |
| Cruciferous vegetables | | | | | | | | |
| Fresh vegetable juice | | | | | | | | |
| **BEANS** | | | | | | | | |
| Total beans and lentils | | | | | | | | |
| **ONIONS** | | | | | | | | |
| Vegetables from the onion family | | | | | | | | |
| **MUSHROOMS** | | | | | | | | |
| Cooked mushrooms | | | | | | | | |
| **BERRIES** *(and other fruit)* | | | | | | | | |
| Berries/pomegranate | | | | | | | | |
| Other fruit | | | | | | | | |
| Dried fruit | | | | | | | | |
| **NUTS AND SEEDS** | | | | | | | | |
| High omega-3: walnuts, chia, hemp, flax | | | | | | | | |
| Other nuts and seeds, avocado | | | | | | | | |
| **LIMITED FOODS** | | | | | | | | |
| Whole grains/starchy vegetables | | | | | | | | |
| Poultry, eggs, dairy, and fish | | | | | | | | |
| Oils | | | | | | | | |
| White potatoes | | | | | | | | |
| Added sodium | | | | | | | | |
| **FOODS TO AVOID** | | | | | | | | |
| Red meats | | | | | | | | |
| Sugar and sweets | | | | | | | | |
| White rice, white flour products, and processed foods | | | | | | | | |
| **SUPPLEMENTS** — *Which supplements did I take today?* | | | | | | | | |
| Multivitamin (no vitamins A or E, beta-carotene, folic acid, copper) | | | | | | | | |
| Vitamin D | | | | | | | | |
| Omega-3 fatty acids | | | | | | | | |
| Other | | | | | | | | |
| **EXERCISE** — *How much did I exercise today?* | | | | | | | | |
| Easy to moderate activity | | | | | | | | |
| Vigorous activity | | | | | | | | |

**TOTAL SCORE:**

## DID I MEET EACH OF MY GOALS TODAY?

| | MON | TUE | WED | THU | FRI | SAT | SUN | MY WEEKLY SUPER IMMUNITY SCORE |
|---|---|---|---|---|---|---|---|---|
| **GREENS** *(and other vegetables)* | | | | | | | | |
| Raw leafy greens | | | | | | | | |
| Other raw vegetables | | | | | | | | |
| Total cooked vegetables | | | | | | | | |
| Cruciferous vegetables | | | | | | | | |
| Fresh vegetable juice | | | | | | | | |
| **BEANS** | | | | | | | | |
| Total beans and lentils | | | | | | | | |
| **ONIONS** | | | | | | | | |
| Vegetables from the onion family | | | | | | | | |
| **MUSHROOMS** | | | | | | | | |
| Cooked mushrooms | | | | | | | | |
| **BERRIES** *(and other fruit)* | | | | | | | | |
| Berries/pomegranate | | | | | | | | |
| Other fruit | | | | | | | | |
| Dried fruit | | | | | | | | |
| **NUTS AND SEEDS** | | | | | | | | |
| High omega-3: walnuts, chia, hemp, flax | | | | | | | | |
| Other nuts and seeds, avocado | | | | | | | | |
| **LIMITED FOODS** | | | | | | | | |
| Whole grains/starchy vegetables | | | | | | | | |
| Poultry, eggs, dairy, and fish | | | | | | | | |
| Oils | | | | | | | | |
| White potatoes | | | | | | | | |
| Added sodium | | | | | | | | |
| **FOODS TO AVOID** | | | | | | | | |
| Red meats | | | | | | | | |
| Sugar and sweets | | | | | | | | |
| White rice, white flour products, and processed foods | | | | | | | | |
| **SUPPLEMENTS — *Which supplements did I take today?*** | | | | | | | | |
| Multivitamin (no vitamins A or E, beta-carotene, folic acid, copper) | | | | | | | | |
| Vitamin D | | | | | | | | |
| Omega-3 fatty acids | | | | | | | | |
| Other | | | | | | | | |
| **EXERCISE — *How much did I exercise today?*** | | | | | | | | |
| Easy to moderate activity | | | | | | | | |
| Vigorous activity | | | | | | | | |

**TOTAL SCORE:**

# WEEKLY CALENDAR

**DID I MEET EACH OF MY GOALS TODAY?**

| | MON | TUE | WED | THU | FRI | SAT | SUN | MY WEEKLY SUPER° IMMUNITY SCORE |
|---|---|---|---|---|---|---|---|---|
| **GREENS** *(and other vegetables)* | | | | | | | | |
| Raw leafy greens | | | | | | | | |
| Other raw vegetables | | | | | | | | |
| Total cooked vegetables | | | | | | | | |
| Cruciferous vegetables | | | | | | | | |
| Fresh vegetable juice | | | | | | | | |
| **BEANS** | | | | | | | | |
| Total beans and lentils | | | | | | | | |
| **ONIONS** | | | | | | | | |
| Vegetables from the onion family | | | | | | | | |
| **MUSHROOMS** | | | | | | | | |
| Cooked mushrooms | | | | | | | | |
| **BERRIES** *(and other fruit)* | | | | | | | | |
| Berries/pomegranate | | | | | | | | |
| Other fruit | | | | | | | | |
| Dried fruit | | | | | | | | |
| **NUTS AND SEEDS** | | | | | | | | |
| High omega-3: walnuts, chia, hemp, flax | | | | | | | | |
| Other nuts and seeds, avocado | | | | | | | | |
| **LIMITED FOODS** | | | | | | | | |
| Whole grains/starchy vegetables | | | | | | | | |
| Poultry, eggs, dairy, and fish | | | | | | | | |
| Oils | | | | | | | | |
| White potatoes | | | | | | | | |
| Added sodium | | | | | | | | |
| **FOODS TO AVOID** | | | | | | | | |
| Red meats | | | | | | | | |
| Sugar and sweets | | | | | | | | |
| White rice, white flour products, and processed foods | | | | | | | | |
| **SUPPLEMENTS — *Which supplements did I take today?*** | | | | | | | | |
| Multivitamin (no vitamins A or E, beta-carotene, folic acid, copper) | | | | | | | | |
| Vitamin D | | | | | | | | |
| Omega-3 fatty acids | | | | | | | | |
| Other | | | | | | | | |
| **EXERCISE — *How much did I exercise today?*** | | | | | | | | |
| Easy to moderate activity | | | | | | | | |
| Vigorous activity | | | | | | | | |

**TOTAL SCORE:**

# WEEKLY CALENDAR

## DID I MEET EACH OF MY GOALS TODAY?

| | MON | TUE | WED | THU | FRI | SAT | SUN | MY WEEKLY SUPER IMMUNITY SCORE |
|---|---|---|---|---|---|---|---|---|
| **GREENS** (and other vegetables) | | | | | | | | |
| Raw leafy greens | | | | | | | | |
| Other raw vegetables | | | | | | | | |
| Total cooked vegetables | | | | | | | | |
| Cruciferous vegetables | | | | | | | | |
| Fresh vegetable juice | | | | | | | | |
| **BEANS** | | | | | | | | |
| Total beans and lentils | | | | | | | | |
| **ONIONS** | | | | | | | | |
| Vegetables from the onion family | | | | | | | | |
| **MUSHROOMS** | | | | | | | | |
| Cooked mushrooms | | | | | | | | |
| **BERRIES** (and other fruit) | | | | | | | | |
| Berries/pomegranate | | | | | | | | |
| Other fruit | | | | | | | | |
| Dried fruit | | | | | | | | |
| **NUTS AND SEEDS** | | | | | | | | |
| High omega-3: walnuts, chia, hemp, flax | | | | | | | | |
| Other nuts and seeds, avocado | | | | | | | | |
| **LIMITED FOODS** | | | | | | | | |
| Whole grains/starchy vegetables | | | | | | | | |
| Poultry, eggs, dairy, and fish | | | | | | | | |
| Oils | | | | | | | | |
| White potatoes | | | | | | | | |
| Added sodium | | | | | | | | |
| **FOODS TO AVOID** | | | | | | | | |
| Red meats | | | | | | | | |
| Sugar and sweets | | | | | | | | |
| White rice, white flour products, and processed foods | | | | | | | | |
| **SUPPLEMENTS — Which supplements did I take today?** | | | | | | | | |
| Multivitamin (no vitamins A or E, beta-carotene, folic acid, copper) | | | | | | | | |
| Vitamin D | | | | | | | | |
| Omega-3 fatty acids | | | | | | | | |
| Other | | | | | | | | |
| **EXERCISE — How much did I exercise today?** | | | | | | | | |
| Easy to moderate activity | | | | | | | | |
| Vigorous activity | | | | | | | | |

**TOTAL SCORE:**

# WEEKLY CALENDAR

**DID I MEET EACH OF MY GOALS TODAY?**

| | MON | TUE | WED | THU | FRI | SAT | SUN | MY WEEKLY SUPER IMMUNITY SCORE |
|---|---|---|---|---|---|---|---|---|
| **GREENS** *(and other vegetables)* | | | | | | | | |
| Raw leafy greens | | | | | | | | |
| Other raw vegetables | | | | | | | | |
| Total cooked vegetables | | | | | | | | |
| Cruciferous vegetables | | | | | | | | |
| Fresh vegetable juice | | | | | | | | |
| **BEANS** | | | | | | | | |
| Total beans and lentils | | | | | | | | |
| **ONIONS** | | | | | | | | |
| Vegetables from the onion family | | | | | | | | |
| **MUSHROOMS** | | | | | | | | |
| Cooked mushrooms | | | | | | | | |
| **BERRIES** *(and other fruit)* | | | | | | | | |
| Berries/pomegranate | | | | | | | | |
| Other fruit | | | | | | | | |
| Dried fruit | | | | | | | | |
| **NUTS AND SEEDS** | | | | | | | | |
| High omega-3: walnuts, chia, hemp, flax | | | | | | | | |
| Other nuts and seeds, avocado | | | | | | | | |
| **LIMITED FOODS** | | | | | | | | |
| Whole grains/starchy vegetables | | | | | | | | |
| Poultry, eggs, dairy, and fish | | | | | | | | |
| Oils | | | | | | | | |
| White potatoes | | | | | | | | |
| Added sodium | | | | | | | | |
| **FOODS TO AVOID** | | | | | | | | |
| Red meats | | | | | | | | |
| Sugar and sweets | | | | | | | | |
| White rice, white flour products, and processed foods | | | | | | | | |
| **SUPPLEMENTS — *Which supplements did I take today?*** | | | | | | | | |
| Multivitamin (no vitamins A or E, beta-carotene, folic acid, copper) | | | | | | | | |
| Vitamin D | | | | | | | | |
| Omega-3 fatty acids | | | | | | | | |
| Other | | | | | | | | |
| **EXERCISE — *How much did I exercise today?*** | | | | | | | | |
| Easy to moderate activity | | | | | | | | |
| Vigorous activity | | | | | | | | |

**TOTAL SCORE:**

# WEEKLY CALENDAR

**DID I MEET EACH OF MY GOALS TODAY?**

| | MON | TUE | WED | THU | FRI | SAT | SUN | MY WEEKLY SUPER IMMUNITY SCORE |
|---|---|---|---|---|---|---|---|---|
| **GREENS** (and other vegetables) | | | | | | | | |
| Raw leafy greens | | | | | | | | |
| Other raw vegetables | | | | | | | | |
| Total cooked vegetables | | | | | | | | |
| Cruciferous vegetables | | | | | | | | |
| Fresh vegetable juice | | | | | | | | |
| **BEANS** | | | | | | | | |
| Total beans and lentils | | | | | | | | |
| **ONIONS** | | | | | | | | |
| Vegetables from the onion family | | | | | | | | |
| **MUSHROOMS** | | | | | | | | |
| Cooked mushrooms | | | | | | | | |
| **BERRIES** (and other fruit) | | | | | | | | |
| Berries/pomegranate | | | | | | | | |
| Other fruit | | | | | | | | |
| Dried fruit | | | | | | | | |
| **NUTS AND SEEDS** | | | | | | | | |
| High omega-3: walnuts, chia, hemp, flax | | | | | | | | |
| Other nuts and seeds, avocado | | | | | | | | |
| **LIMITED FOODS** | | | | | | | | |
| Whole grains/starchy vegetables | | | | | | | | |
| Poultry, eggs, dairy, and fish | | | | | | | | |
| Oils | | | | | | | | |
| White potatoes | | | | | | | | |
| Added sodium | | | | | | | | |
| **FOODS TO AVOID** | | | | | | | | |
| Red meats | | | | | | | | |
| Sugar and sweets | | | | | | | | |
| White rice, white flour products, and processed foods | | | | | | | | |
| **SUPPLEMENTS — Which supplements did I take today?** | | | | | | | | |
| Multivitamin (no vitamins A or E, beta-carotene, folic acid, copper) | | | | | | | | |
| Vitamin D | | | | | | | | |
| Omega-3 fatty acids | | | | | | | | |
| Other | | | | | | | | |
| **EXERCISE — How much did I exercise today?** | | | | | | | | |
| Easy to moderate activity | | | | | | | | |
| Vigorous activity | | | | | | | | |

**TOTAL SCORE:**

## WEEKLY CALENDAR

**DID I MEET EACH OF MY GOALS TODAY?**

| | MON | TUE | WED | THU | FRI | SAT | SUN | MY WEEKLY SUPER IMMUNITY SCORE |
|---|---|---|---|---|---|---|---|---|
| **GREENS** *(and other vegetables)* | | | | | | | | |
| Raw leafy greens | | | | | | | | |
| Other raw vegetables | | | | | | | | |
| Total cooked vegetables | | | | | | | | |
| Cruciferous vegetables | | | | | | | | |
| Fresh vegetable juice | | | | | | | | |
| **BEANS** | | | | | | | | |
| Total beans and lentils | | | | | | | | |
| **ONIONS** | | | | | | | | |
| Vegetables from the onion family | | | | | | | | |
| **MUSHROOMS** | | | | | | | | |
| Cooked mushrooms | | | | | | | | |
| **BERRIES** *(and other fruit)* | | | | | | | | |
| Berries/pomegranate | | | | | | | | |
| Other fruit | | | | | | | | |
| Dried fruit | | | | | | | | |
| **NUTS AND SEEDS** | | | | | | | | |
| High omega-3: walnuts, chia, hemp, flax | | | | | | | | |
| Other nuts and seeds, avocado | | | | | | | | |
| **LIMITED FOODS** | | | | | | | | |
| Whole grains/starchy vegetables | | | | | | | | |
| Poultry, eggs, dairy, and fish | | | | | | | | |
| Oils | | | | | | | | |
| White potatoes | | | | | | | | |
| Added sodium | | | | | | | | |
| **FOODS TO AVOID** | | | | | | | | |
| Red meats | | | | | | | | |
| Sugar and sweets | | | | | | | | |
| White rice, white flour products, and processed foods | | | | | | | | |
| **SUPPLEMENTS — *Which supplements did I take today?*** | | | | | | | | |
| Multivitamin (no vitamins A or E, beta-carotene, folic acid, copper) | | | | | | | | |
| Vitamin D | | | | | | | | |
| Omega-3 fatty acids | | | | | | | | |
| Other | | | | | | | | |
| **EXERCISE — *How much did I exercise today?*** | | | | | | | | |
| Easy to moderate activity | | | | | | | | |
| Vigorous activity | | | | | | | | |

**TOTAL SCORE:**

# WEEKLY CALENDAR

**DID I MEET EACH OF MY GOALS TODAY?**

| | MON | TUE | WED | THU | FRI | SAT | SUN | MY WEEKLY SUPER IMMUNITY SCORE |
|---|---|---|---|---|---|---|---|---|
| **GREENS** *(and other vegetables)* | | | | | | | | |
| Raw leafy greens | | | | | | | | |
| Other raw vegetables | | | | | | | | |
| Total cooked vegetables | | | | | | | | |
| Cruciferous vegetables | | | | | | | | |
| Fresh vegetable juice | | | | | | | | |
| **BEANS** | | | | | | | | |
| Total beans and lentils | | | | | | | | |
| **ONIONS** | | | | | | | | |
| Vegetables from the onion family | | | | | | | | |
| **MUSHROOMS** | | | | | | | | |
| Cooked mushrooms | | | | | | | | |
| **BERRIES** *(and other fruit)* | | | | | | | | |
| Berries/pomegranate | | | | | | | | |
| Other fruit | | | | | | | | |
| Dried fruit | | | | | | | | |
| **NUTS AND SEEDS** | | | | | | | | |
| High omega-3: walnuts, chia, hemp, flax | | | | | | | | |
| Other nuts and seeds, avocado | | | | | | | | |
| **LIMITED FOODS** | | | | | | | | |
| Whole grains/starchy vegetables | | | | | | | | |
| Poultry, eggs, dairy, and fish | | | | | | | | |
| Oils | | | | | | | | |
| White potatoes | | | | | | | | |
| Added sodium | | | | | | | | |
| **FOODS TO AVOID** | | | | | | | | |
| Red meats | | | | | | | | |
| Sugar and sweets | | | | | | | | |
| White rice, white flour products, and processed foods | | | | | | | | |
| **SUPPLEMENTS — *Which supplements did I take today?*** | | | | | | | | |
| Multivitamin (no vitamins A or E, beta-carotene, folic acid, copper) | | | | | | | | |
| Vitamin D | | | | | | | | |
| Omega-3 fatty acids | | | | | | | | |
| Other | | | | | | | | |
| **EXERCISE — *How much did I exercise today?*** | | | | | | | | |
| Easy to moderate activity | | | | | | | | |
| Vigorous activity | | | | | | | | |

**TOTAL SCORE:** [        ]

## WEEKLY CALENDAR

**DID I MEET EACH OF MY GOALS TODAY?**

| | MON | TUE | WED | THU | FRI | SAT | SUN | MY WEEKLY SUPER IMMUNITY SCORE |
|---|---|---|---|---|---|---|---|---|
| **GREENS** *(and other vegetables)* | | | | | | | | |
| Raw leafy greens | | | | | | | | |
| Other raw vegetables | | | | | | | | |
| Total cooked vegetables | | | | | | | | |
| Cruciferous vegetables | | | | | | | | |
| Fresh vegetable juice | | | | | | | | |
| **BEANS** | | | | | | | | |
| Total beans and lentils | | | | | | | | |
| **ONIONS** | | | | | | | | |
| Vegetables from the onion family | | | | | | | | |
| **MUSHROOMS** | | | | | | | | |
| Cooked mushrooms | | | | | | | | |
| **BERRIES** *(and other fruit)* | | | | | | | | |
| Berries/pomegranate | | | | | | | | |
| Other fruit | | | | | | | | |
| Dried fruit | | | | | | | | |
| **NUTS AND SEEDS** | | | | | | | | |
| High omega-3: walnuts, chia, hemp, flax | | | | | | | | |
| Other nuts and seeds, avocado | | | | | | | | |
| **LIMITED FOODS** | | | | | | | | |
| Whole grains/starchy vegetables | | | | | | | | |
| Poultry, eggs, dairy, and fish | | | | | | | | |
| Oils | | | | | | | | |
| White potatoes | | | | | | | | |
| Added sodium | | | | | | | | |
| **FOODS TO AVOID** | | | | | | | | |
| Red meats | | | | | | | | |
| Sugar and sweets | | | | | | | | |
| White rice, white flour products, and processed foods | | | | | | | | |
| **SUPPLEMENTS — *Which supplements did I take today?*** | | | | | | | | |
| Multivitamin (no vitamins A or E, beta-carotene, folic acid, copper) | | | | | | | | |
| Vitamin D | | | | | | | | |
| Omega-3 fatty acids | | | | | | | | |
| Other | | | | | | | | |
| **EXERCISE — *How much did I exercise today?*** | | | | | | | | |
| Easy to moderate activity | | | | | | | | |
| Vigorous activity | | | | | | | | |

**TOTAL SCORE:** [　　　　]

# WEEKLY CALENDAR

## DID I MEET EACH OF MY GOALS TODAY?

| | MON | TUE | WED | THU | FRI | SAT | SUN | MY WEEKLY SUPER IMMUNITY SCORE |
|---|---|---|---|---|---|---|---|---|
| **GREENS** (and other vegetables) | | | | | | | | |
| Raw leafy greens | | | | | | | | |
| Other raw vegetables | | | | | | | | |
| Total cooked vegetables | | | | | | | | |
| Cruciferous vegetables | | | | | | | | |
| Fresh vegetable juice | | | | | | | | |
| **BEANS** | | | | | | | | |
| Total beans and lentils | | | | | | | | |
| **ONIONS** | | | | | | | | |
| Vegetables from the onion family | | | | | | | | |
| **MUSHROOMS** | | | | | | | | |
| Cooked mushrooms | | | | | | | | |
| **BERRIES** (and other fruit) | | | | | | | | |
| Berries/pomegranate | | | | | | | | |
| Other fruit | | | | | | | | |
| Dried fruit | | | | | | | | |
| **NUTS AND SEEDS** | | | | | | | | |
| High omega-3: walnuts, chia, hemp, flax | | | | | | | | |
| Other nuts and seeds, avocado | | | | | | | | |
| **LIMITED FOODS** | | | | | | | | |
| Whole grains/starchy vegetables | | | | | | | | |
| Poultry, eggs, dairy, and fish | | | | | | | | |
| Oils | | | | | | | | |
| White potatoes | | | | | | | | |
| Added sodium | | | | | | | | |
| **FOODS TO AVOID** | | | | | | | | |
| Red meats | | | | | | | | |
| Sugar and sweets | | | | | | | | |
| White rice, white flour products, and processed foods | | | | | | | | |
| **SUPPLEMENTS — *Which supplements did I take today?*** | | | | | | | | |
| Multivitamin (no vitamins A or E, beta-carotene, folic acid, copper) | | | | | | | | |
| Vitamin D | | | | | | | | |
| Omega-3 fatty acids | | | | | | | | |
| Other | | | | | | | | |
| **EXERCISE — *How much did I exercise today?*** | | | | | | | | |
| Easy to moderate activity | | | | | | | | |
| Vigorous activity | | | | | | | | |

**TOTAL SCORE:**

## WEEKLY CALENDAR

**DID I MEET EACH OF MY GOALS TODAY?**

| | MON | TUE | WED | THU | FRI | SAT | SUN | MY WEEKLY SUPER IMMUNITY SCORE |
|---|---|---|---|---|---|---|---|---|
| **GREENS** (and other vegetables) | | | | | | | | |
| Raw leafy greens | | | | | | | | |
| Other raw vegetables | | | | | | | | |
| Total cooked vegetables | | | | | | | | |
| Cruciferous vegetables | | | | | | | | |
| Fresh vegetable juice | | | | | | | | |
| **BEANS** | | | | | | | | |
| Total beans and lentils | | | | | | | | |
| **ONIONS** | | | | | | | | |
| Vegetables from the onion family | | | | | | | | |
| **MUSHROOMS** | | | | | | | | |
| Cooked mushrooms | | | | | | | | |
| **BERRIES** (and other fruit) | | | | | | | | |
| Berries/pomegranate | | | | | | | | |
| Other fruit | | | | | | | | |
| Dried fruit | | | | | | | | |
| **NUTS AND SEEDS** | | | | | | | | |
| High omega-3: walnuts, chia, hemp, flax | | | | | | | | |
| Other nuts and seeds, avocado | | | | | | | | |
| **LIMITED FOODS** | | | | | | | | |
| Whole grains/starchy vegetables | | | | | | | | |
| Poultry, eggs, dairy, and fish | | | | | | | | |
| Oils | | | | | | | | |
| White potatoes | | | | | | | | |
| Added sodium | | | | | | | | |
| **FOODS TO AVOID** | | | | | | | | |
| Red meats | | | | | | | | |
| Sugar and sweets | | | | | | | | |
| White rice, white flour products, and processed foods | | | | | | | | |
| **SUPPLEMENTS** — *Which supplements did I take today?* | | | | | | | | |
| Multivitamin (no vitamins A or E, beta-carotene, folic acid, copper) | | | | | | | | |
| Vitamin D | | | | | | | | |
| Omega-3 fatty acids | | | | | | | | |
| Other | | | | | | | | |
| **EXERCISE** — *How much did I exercise today?* | | | | | | | | |
| Easy to moderate activity | | | | | | | | |
| Vigorous activity | | | | | | | | |

**TOTAL SCORE:**

## WEEKLY CALENDAR

**DID I MEET EACH OF MY GOALS TODAY?**

| | MON | TUE | WED | THU | FRI | SAT | SUN | MY WEEKLY SUPER IMMUNITY SCORE |
|---|---|---|---|---|---|---|---|---|
| **GREENS** (*and other vegetables*) | | | | | | | | |
| Raw leafy greens | | | | | | | | |
| Other raw vegetables | | | | | | | | |
| Total cooked vegetables | | | | | | | | |
| Cruciferous vegetables | | | | | | | | |
| Fresh vegetable juice | | | | | | | | |
| **BEANS** | | | | | | | | |
| Total beans and lentils | | | | | | | | |
| **ONIONS** | | | | | | | | |
| Vegetables from the onion family | | | | | | | | |
| **MUSHROOMS** | | | | | | | | |
| Cooked mushrooms | | | | | | | | |
| **BERRIES** (*and other fruit*) | | | | | | | | |
| Berries/pomegranate | | | | | | | | |
| Other fruit | | | | | | | | |
| Dried fruit | | | | | | | | |
| **NUTS AND SEEDS** | | | | | | | | |
| High omega-3: walnuts, chia, hemp, flax | | | | | | | | |
| Other nuts and seeds, avocado | | | | | | | | |
| **LIMITED FOODS** | | | | | | | | |
| Whole grains/starchy vegetables | | | | | | | | |
| Poultry, eggs, dairy, and fish | | | | | | | | |
| Oils | | | | | | | | |
| White potatoes | | | | | | | | |
| Added sodium | | | | | | | | |
| **FOODS TO AVOID** | | | | | | | | |
| Red meats | | | | | | | | |
| Sugar and sweets | | | | | | | | |
| White rice, white flour products, and processed foods | | | | | | | | |
| **SUPPLEMENTS — *Which supplements did I take today?*** | | | | | | | | |
| Multivitamin (no vitamins A or E, beta-carotene, folic acid, copper) | | | | | | | | |
| Vitamin D | | | | | | | | |
| Omega-3 fatty acids | | | | | | | | |
| Other | | | | | | | | |
| **EXERCISE — *How much did I exercise today?*** | | | | | | | | |
| Easy to moderate activity | | | | | | | | |
| Vigorous activity | | | | | | | | |

**TOTAL SCORE:**

## WEEKLY CALENDAR

**DID I MEET EACH OF MY GOALS TODAY?**

| | MON | TUE | WED | THU | FRI | SAT | SUN | MY WEEKLY SUPER IMMUNITY SCORE |
|---|---|---|---|---|---|---|---|---|
| **GREENS** *(and other vegetables)* | | | | | | | | |
| Raw leafy greens | | | | | | | | |
| Other raw vegetables | | | | | | | | |
| Total cooked vegetables | | | | | | | | |
| Cruciferous vegetables | | | | | | | | |
| Fresh vegetable juice | | | | | | | | |
| **BEANS** | | | | | | | | |
| Total beans and lentils | | | | | | | | |
| **ONIONS** | | | | | | | | |
| Vegetables from the onion family | | | | | | | | |
| **MUSHROOMS** | | | | | | | | |
| Cooked mushrooms | | | | | | | | |
| **BERRIES** *(and other fruit)* | | | | | | | | |
| Berries/pomegranate | | | | | | | | |
| Other fruit | | | | | | | | |
| Dried fruit | | | | | | | | |
| **NUTS AND SEEDS** | | | | | | | | |
| High omega-3: walnuts, chia, hemp, flax | | | | | | | | |
| Other nuts and seeds, avocado | | | | | | | | |
| **LIMITED FOODS** | | | | | | | | |
| Whole grains/starchy vegetables | | | | | | | | |
| Poultry, eggs, dairy, and fish | | | | | | | | |
| Oils | | | | | | | | |
| White potatoes | | | | | | | | |
| Added sodium | | | | | | | | |
| **FOODS TO AVOID** | | | | | | | | |
| Red meats | | | | | | | | |
| Sugar and sweets | | | | | | | | |
| White rice, white flour products, and processed foods | | | | | | | | |
| **SUPPLEMENTS — *Which supplements did I take today?*** | | | | | | | | |
| Multivitamin (no vitamins A or E, beta-carotene, folic acid, copper) | | | | | | | | |
| Vitamin D | | | | | | | | |
| Omega-3 fatty acids | | | | | | | | |
| Other | | | | | | | | |
| **EXERCISE — *How much did I exercise today?*** | | | | | | | | |
| Easy to moderate activity | | | | | | | | |
| Vigorous activity | | | | | | | | |

**TOTAL SCORE:**

## WEEKLY CALENDAR

**DID I MEET EACH OF MY GOALS TODAY?**

| | MON | TUE | WED | THU | FRI | SAT | SUN | MY WEEKLY SUPER IMMUNITY SCORE |
|---|---|---|---|---|---|---|---|---|
| **GREENS** *(and other vegetables)* | | | | | | | | |
| Raw leafy greens | | | | | | | | |
| Other raw vegetables | | | | | | | | |
| Total cooked vegetables | | | | | | | | |
| Cruciferous vegetables | | | | | | | | |
| Fresh vegetable juice | | | | | | | | |
| **BEANS** | | | | | | | | |
| Total beans and lentils | | | | | | | | |
| **ONIONS** | | | | | | | | |
| Vegetables from the onion family | | | | | | | | |
| **MUSHROOMS** | | | | | | | | |
| Cooked mushrooms | | | | | | | | |
| **BERRIES** *(and other fruit)* | | | | | | | | |
| Berries/pomegranate | | | | | | | | |
| Other fruit | | | | | | | | |
| Dried fruit | | | | | | | | |
| **NUTS AND SEEDS** | | | | | | | | |
| High omega-3: walnuts, chia, hemp, flax | | | | | | | | |
| Other nuts and seeds, avocado | | | | | | | | |
| **LIMITED FOODS** | | | | | | | | |
| Whole grains/starchy vegetables | | | | | | | | |
| Poultry, eggs, dairy, and fish | | | | | | | | |
| Oils | | | | | | | | |
| White potatoes | | | | | | | | |
| Added sodium | | | | | | | | |
| **FOODS TO AVOID** | | | | | | | | |
| Red meats | | | | | | | | |
| Sugar and sweets | | | | | | | | |
| White rice, white flour products, and processed foods | | | | | | | | |
| **SUPPLEMENTS — *Which supplements did I take today?*** | | | | | | | | |
| Multivitamin (no vitamins A or E, beta-carotene, folic acid, copper) | | | | | | | | |
| Vitamin D | | | | | | | | |
| Omega-3 fatty acids | | | | | | | | |
| Other | | | | | | | | |
| **EXERCISE — *How much did I exercise today?*** | | | | | | | | |
| Easy to moderate activity | | | | | | | | |
| Vigorous activity | | | | | | | | |

**TOTAL SCORE:**

## WEEKLY CALENDAR

**DID I MEET EACH OF MY GOALS TODAY?**

| | MON | TUE | WED | THU | FRI | SAT | SUN | MY WEEKLY SUPER IMMUNITY SCORE |
|---|---|---|---|---|---|---|---|---|
| **GREENS** *(and other vegetables)* | | | | | | | | |
| Raw leafy greens | | | | | | | | |
| Other raw vegetables | | | | | | | | |
| Total cooked vegetables | | | | | | | | |
| Cruciferous vegetables | | | | | | | | |
| Fresh vegetable juice | | | | | | | | |
| **BEANS** | | | | | | | | |
| Total beans and lentils | | | | | | | | |
| **ONIONS** | | | | | | | | |
| Vegetables from the onion family | | | | | | | | |
| **MUSHROOMS** | | | | | | | | |
| Cooked mushrooms | | | | | | | | |
| **BERRIES** *(and other fruit)* | | | | | | | | |
| Berries/pomegranate | | | | | | | | |
| Other fruit | | | | | | | | |
| Dried fruit | | | | | | | | |
| **NUTS AND SEEDS** | | | | | | | | |
| High omega-3: walnuts, chia, hemp, flax | | | | | | | | |
| Other nuts and seeds, avocado | | | | | | | | |
| **LIMITED FOODS** | | | | | | | | |
| Whole grains/starchy vegetables | | | | | | | | |
| Poultry, eggs, dairy, and fish | | | | | | | | |
| Oils | | | | | | | | |
| White potatoes | | | | | | | | |
| Added sodium | | | | | | | | |
| **FOODS TO AVOID** | | | | | | | | |
| Red meats | | | | | | | | |
| Sugar and sweets | | | | | | | | |
| White rice, white flour products, and processed foods | | | | | | | | |
| **SUPPLEMENTS** — *Which supplements did I take today?* | | | | | | | | |
| Multivitamin (no vitamins A or E, beta-carotene, folic acid, copper) | | | | | | | | |
| Vitamin D | | | | | | | | |
| Omega-3 fatty acids | | | | | | | | |
| Other | | | | | | | | |
| **EXERCISE** — *How much did I exercise today?* | | | | | | | | |
| Easy to moderate activity | | | | | | | | |
| Vigorous activity | | | | | | | | |

**TOTAL SCORE:**

**DID I MEET EACH OF MY GOALS TODAY?**

| | MON | TUE | WED | THU | FRI | SAT | SUN | MY WEEKLY SUPER IMMUNITY SCORE |
|---|---|---|---|---|---|---|---|---|
| **GREENS** *(and other vegetables)* | | | | | | | | |
| Raw leafy greens | | | | | | | | |
| Other raw vegetables | | | | | | | | |
| Total cooked vegetables | | | | | | | | |
| Cruciferous vegetables | | | | | | | | |
| Fresh vegetable juice | | | | | | | | |
| **BEANS** | | | | | | | | |
| Total beans and lentils | | | | | | | | |
| **ONIONS** | | | | | | | | |
| Vegetables from the onion family | | | | | | | | |
| **MUSHROOMS** | | | | | | | | |
| Cooked mushrooms | | | | | | | | |
| **BERRIES** *(and other fruit)* | | | | | | | | |
| Berries/pomegranate | | | | | | | | |
| Other fruit | | | | | | | | |
| Dried fruit | | | | | | | | |
| **NUTS AND SEEDS** | | | | | | | | |
| High omega-3: walnuts, chia, hemp, flax | | | | | | | | |
| Other nuts and seeds, avocado | | | | | | | | |
| **LIMITED FOODS** | | | | | | | | |
| Whole grains/starchy vegetables | | | | | | | | |
| Poultry, eggs, dairy, and fish | | | | | | | | |
| Oils | | | | | | | | |
| White potatoes | | | | | | | | |
| Added sodium | | | | | | | | |
| **FOODS TO AVOID** | | | | | | | | |
| Red meats | | | | | | | | |
| Sugar and sweets | | | | | | | | |
| White rice, white flour products, and processed foods | | | | | | | | |
| **SUPPLEMENTS — *Which supplements did I take today?*** | | | | | | | | |
| Multivitamin (no vitamins A or E, beta-carotene, folic acid, copper) | | | | | | | | |
| Vitamin D | | | | | | | | |
| Omega-3 fatty acids | | | | | | | | |
| Other | | | | | | | | |
| **EXERCISE — *How much did I exercise today?*** | | | | | | | | |
| Easy to moderate activity | | | | | | | | |
| Vigorous activity | | | | | | | | |

**TOTAL SCORE:**

# WEEKLY CALENDAR

**DID I MEET EACH OF MY GOALS TODAY?**

| | MON | TUE | WED | THU | FRI | SAT | SUN | MY WEEKLY SUPER IMMUNITY SCORE |
|---|---|---|---|---|---|---|---|---|
| **GREENS** (and other vegetables) | | | | | | | | |
| Raw leafy greens | | | | | | | | |
| Other raw vegetables | | | | | | | | |
| Total cooked vegetables | | | | | | | | |
| Cruciferous vegetables | | | | | | | | |
| Fresh vegetable juice | | | | | | | | |
| **BEANS** | | | | | | | | |
| Total beans and lentils | | | | | | | | |
| **ONIONS** | | | | | | | | |
| Vegetables from the onion family | | | | | | | | |
| **MUSHROOMS** | | | | | | | | |
| Cooked mushrooms | | | | | | | | |
| **BERRIES** (and other fruit) | | | | | | | | |
| Berries/pomegranate | | | | | | | | |
| Other fruit | | | | | | | | |
| Dried fruit | | | | | | | | |
| **NUTS AND SEEDS** | | | | | | | | |
| High omega-3: walnuts, chia, hemp, flax | | | | | | | | |
| Other nuts and seeds, avocado | | | | | | | | |
| **LIMITED FOODS** | | | | | | | | |
| Whole grains/starchy vegetables | | | | | | | | |
| Poultry, eggs, dairy, and fish | | | | | | | | |
| Oils | | | | | | | | |
| White potatoes | | | | | | | | |
| Added sodium | | | | | | | | |
| **FOODS TO AVOID** | | | | | | | | |
| Red meats | | | | | | | | |
| Sugar and sweets | | | | | | | | |
| White rice, white flour products, and processed foods | | | | | | | | |
| **SUPPLEMENTS** — *Which supplements did I take today?* | | | | | | | | |
| Multivitamin (no vitamins A or E, beta-carotene, folic acid, copper) | | | | | | | | |
| Vitamin D | | | | | | | | |
| Omega-3 fatty acids | | | | | | | | |
| Other | | | | | | | | |
| **EXERCISE** — *How much did I exercise today?* | | | | | | | | |
| Easy to moderate activity | | | | | | | | |
| Vigorous activity | | | | | | | | |

**TOTAL SCORE:**

## WEEKLY CALENDAR

**DID I MEET EACH OF MY GOALS TODAY?**

| | MON | TUE | WED | THU | FRI | SAT | SUN | MY WEEKLY SUPER IMMUNITY SCORE |
|---|---|---|---|---|---|---|---|---|
| **GREENS** (*and other vegetables*) | | | | | | | | |
| Raw leafy greens | | | | | | | | |
| Other raw vegetables | | | | | | | | |
| Total cooked vegetables | | | | | | | | |
| Cruciferous vegetables | | | | | | | | |
| Fresh vegetable juice | | | | | | | | |
| **BEANS** | | | | | | | | |
| Total beans and lentils | | | | | | | | |
| **ONIONS** | | | | | | | | |
| Vegetables from the onion family | | | | | | | | |
| **MUSHROOMS** | | | | | | | | |
| Cooked mushrooms | | | | | | | | |
| **BERRIES** (*and other fruit*) | | | | | | | | |
| Berries/pomegranate | | | | | | | | |
| Other fruit | | | | | | | | |
| Dried fruit | | | | | | | | |
| **NUTS AND SEEDS** | | | | | | | | |
| High omega-3: walnuts, chia, hemp, flax | | | | | | | | |
| Other nuts and seeds, avocado | | | | | | | | |
| **LIMITED FOODS** | | | | | | | | |
| Whole grains/starchy vegetables | | | | | | | | |
| Poultry, eggs, dairy, and fish | | | | | | | | |
| Oils | | | | | | | | |
| White potatoes | | | | | | | | |
| Added sodium | | | | | | | | |
| **FOODS TO AVOID** | | | | | | | | |
| Red meats | | | | | | | | |
| Sugar and sweets | | | | | | | | |
| White rice, white flour products, and processed foods | | | | | | | | |
| **SUPPLEMENTS — *Which supplements did I take today?*** | | | | | | | | |
| Multivitamin (no vitamins A or E, beta-carotene, folic acid, copper) | | | | | | | | |
| Vitamin D | | | | | | | | |
| Omega-3 fatty acids | | | | | | | | |
| Other | | | | | | | | |
| **EXERCISE — *How much did I exercise today?*** | | | | | | | | |
| Easy to moderate activity | | | | | | | | |
| Vigorous activity | | | | | | | | |

**TOTAL SCORE:**

## WEEKLY CALENDAR

### DID I MEET EACH OF MY GOALS TODAY?

| | MON | TUE | WED | THU | FRI | SAT | SUN | MY WEEKLY SUPER IMMUNITY SCORE |
|---|---|---|---|---|---|---|---|---|
| **GREENS** *(and other vegetables)* | | | | | | | | |
| Raw leafy greens | | | | | | | | |
| Other raw vegetables | | | | | | | | |
| Total cooked vegetables | | | | | | | | |
| Cruciferous vegetables | | | | | | | | |
| Fresh vegetable juice | | | | | | | | |
| **BEANS** | | | | | | | | |
| Total beans and lentils | | | | | | | | |
| **ONIONS** | | | | | | | | |
| Vegetables from the onion family | | | | | | | | |
| **MUSHROOMS** | | | | | | | | |
| Cooked mushrooms | | | | | | | | |
| **BERRIES** *(and other fruit)* | | | | | | | | |
| Berries/pomegranate | | | | | | | | |
| Other fruit | | | | | | | | |
| Dried fruit | | | | | | | | |
| **NUTS AND SEEDS** | | | | | | | | |
| High omega-3: walnuts, chia, hemp, flax | | | | | | | | |
| Other nuts and seeds, avocado | | | | | | | | |
| **LIMITED FOODS** | | | | | | | | |
| Whole grains/starchy vegetables | | | | | | | | |
| Poultry, eggs, dairy, and fish | | | | | | | | |
| Oils | | | | | | | | |
| White potatoes | | | | | | | | |
| Added sodium | | | | | | | | |
| **FOODS TO AVOID** | | | | | | | | |
| Red meats | | | | | | | | |
| Sugar and sweets | | | | | | | | |
| White rice, white flour products, and processed foods | | | | | | | | |
| **SUPPLEMENTS — *Which supplements did I take today?*** | | | | | | | | |
| Multivitamin (no vitamins A or E, beta-carotene, folic acid, copper) | | | | | | | | |
| Vitamin D | | | | | | | | |
| Omega-3 fatty acids | | | | | | | | |
| Other | | | | | | | | |
| **EXERCISE — *How much did I exercise today?*** | | | | | | | | |
| Easy to moderate activity | | | | | | | | |
| Vigorous activity | | | | | | | | |

**TOTAL SCORE:**

## WEEKLY CALENDAR

**DID I MEET EACH OF MY GOALS TODAY?**

| | MON | TUE | WED | THU | FRI | SAT | SUN | MY WEEKLY SUPER IMMUNITY SCORE |
|---|---|---|---|---|---|---|---|---|
| **GREENS** (and other vegetables) | | | | | | | | |
| Raw leafy greens | | | | | | | | |
| Other raw vegetables | | | | | | | | |
| Total cooked vegetables | | | | | | | | |
| Cruciferous vegetables | | | | | | | | |
| Fresh vegetable juice | | | | | | | | |
| **BEANS** | | | | | | | | |
| Total beans and lentils | | | | | | | | |
| **ONIONS** | | | | | | | | |
| Vegetables from the onion family | | | | | | | | |
| **MUSHROOMS** | | | | | | | | |
| Cooked mushrooms | | | | | | | | |
| **BERRIES** (and other fruit) | | | | | | | | |
| Berries/pomegranate | | | | | | | | |
| Other fruit | | | | | | | | |
| Dried fruit | | | | | | | | |
| **NUTS AND SEEDS** | | | | | | | | |
| High omega-3: walnuts, chia, hemp, flax | | | | | | | | |
| Other nuts and seeds, avocado | | | | | | | | |
| **LIMITED FOODS** | | | | | | | | |
| Whole grains/starchy vegetables | | | | | | | | |
| Poultry, eggs, dairy, and fish | | | | | | | | |
| Oils | | | | | | | | |
| White potatoes | | | | | | | | |
| Added sodium | | | | | | | | |
| **FOODS TO AVOID** | | | | | | | | |
| Red meats | | | | | | | | |
| Sugar and sweets | | | | | | | | |
| White rice, white flour products, and processed foods | | | | | | | | |
| **SUPPLEMENTS** — *Which supplements did I take today?* | | | | | | | | |
| Multivitamin (no vitamins A or E, beta-carotene, folic acid, copper) | | | | | | | | |
| Vitamin D | | | | | | | | |
| Omega-3 fatty acids | | | | | | | | |
| Other | | | | | | | | |
| **EXERCISE** — *How much did I exercise today?* | | | | | | | | |
| Easy to moderate activity | | | | | | | | |
| Vigorous activity | | | | | | | | |

**TOTAL SCORE:**

## WEEKLY CALENDAR

**DID I MEET EACH OF MY GOALS TODAY?**

| | MON | TUE | WED | THU | FRI | SAT | SUN | MY WEEKLY SUPER IMMUNITY SCORE |
|---|---|---|---|---|---|---|---|---|
| **GREENS** *(and other vegetables)* | | | | | | | | |
| Raw leafy greens | | | | | | | | |
| Other raw vegetables | | | | | | | | |
| Total cooked vegetables | | | | | | | | |
| Cruciferous vegetables | | | | | | | | |
| Fresh vegetable juice | | | | | | | | |
| **BEANS** | | | | | | | | |
| Total beans and lentils | | | | | | | | |
| **ONIONS** | | | | | | | | |
| Vegetables from the onion family | | | | | | | | |
| **MUSHROOMS** | | | | | | | | |
| Cooked mushrooms | | | | | | | | |
| **BERRIES** *(and other fruit)* | | | | | | | | |
| Berries/pomegranate | | | | | | | | |
| Other fruit | | | | | | | | |
| Dried fruit | | | | | | | | |
| **NUTS AND SEEDS** | | | | | | | | |
| High omega-3: walnuts, chia, hemp, flax | | | | | | | | |
| Other nuts and seeds, avocado | | | | | | | | |
| **LIMITED FOODS** | | | | | | | | |
| Whole grains/starchy vegetables | | | | | | | | |
| Poultry, eggs, dairy, and fish | | | | | | | | |
| Oils | | | | | | | | |
| White potatoes | | | | | | | | |
| Added sodium | | | | | | | | |
| **FOODS TO AVOID** | | | | | | | | |
| Red meats | | | | | | | | |
| Sugar and sweets | | | | | | | | |
| White rice, white flour products, and processed foods | | | | | | | | |
| **SUPPLEMENTS — *Which supplements did I take today?*** | | | | | | | | |
| Multivitamin (no vitamins A or E, beta-carotene, folic acid, copper) | | | | | | | | |
| Vitamin D | | | | | | | | |
| Omega-3 fatty acids | | | | | | | | |
| Other | | | | | | | | |
| **EXERCISE — *How much did I exercise today?*** | | | | | | | | |
| Easy to moderate activity | | | | | | | | |
| Vigorous activity | | | | | | | | |

**TOTAL SCORE:**

## WEEKLY CALENDAR

**DID I MEET EACH OF MY GOALS TODAY?**

| | MON | TUE | WED | THU | FRI | SAT | SUN | MY WEEKLY SUPER IMMUNITY SCORE |
|---|---|---|---|---|---|---|---|---|
| **GREENS** *(and other vegetables)* | | | | | | | | |
| Raw leafy greens | | | | | | | | |
| Other raw vegetables | | | | | | | | |
| Total cooked vegetables | | | | | | | | |
| Cruciferous vegetables | | | | | | | | |
| Fresh vegetable juice | | | | | | | | |
| **BEANS** | | | | | | | | |
| Total beans and lentils | | | | | | | | |
| **ONIONS** | | | | | | | | |
| Vegetables from the onion family | | | | | | | | |
| **MUSHROOMS** | | | | | | | | |
| Cooked mushrooms | | | | | | | | |
| **BERRIES** *(and other fruit)* | | | | | | | | |
| Berries/pomegranate | | | | | | | | |
| Other fruit | | | | | | | | |
| Dried fruit | | | | | | | | |
| **NUTS AND SEEDS** | | | | | | | | |
| High omega-3: walnuts, chia, hemp, flax | | | | | | | | |
| Other nuts and seeds, avocado | | | | | | | | |
| **LIMITED FOODS** | | | | | | | | |
| Whole grains/starchy vegetables | | | | | | | | |
| Poultry, eggs, dairy, and fish | | | | | | | | |
| Oils | | | | | | | | |
| White potatoes | | | | | | | | |
| Added sodium | | | | | | | | |
| **FOODS TO AVOID** | | | | | | | | |
| Red meats | | | | | | | | |
| Sugar and sweets | | | | | | | | |
| White rice, white flour products, and processed foods | | | | | | | | |
| **SUPPLEMENTS** — *Which supplements did I take today?* | | | | | | | | |
| Multivitamin (no vitamins A or E, beta-carotene, folic acid, copper) | | | | | | | | |
| Vitamin D | | | | | | | | |
| Omega-3 fatty acids | | | | | | | | |
| Other | | | | | | | | |
| **EXERCISE** — *How much did I exercise today?* | | | | | | | | |
| Easy to moderate activity | | | | | | | | |
| Vigorous activity | | | | | | | | |

**TOTAL SCORE:**

## WEEKLY CALENDAR

**DID I MEET EACH OF MY GOALS TODAY?**

| | MON | TUE | WED | THU | FRI | SAT | SUN | MY WEEKLY SUPER IMMUNITY SCORE |
|---|---|---|---|---|---|---|---|---|
| **GREENS** *(and other vegetables)* | | | | | | | | |
| Raw leafy greens | | | | | | | | |
| Other raw vegetables | | | | | | | | |
| Total cooked vegetables | | | | | | | | |
| Cruciferous vegetables | | | | | | | | |
| Fresh vegetable juice | | | | | | | | |
| **BEANS** | | | | | | | | |
| Total beans and lentils | | | | | | | | |
| **ONIONS** | | | | | | | | |
| Vegetables from the onion family | | | | | | | | |
| **MUSHROOMS** | | | | | | | | |
| Cooked mushrooms | | | | | | | | |
| **BERRIES** *(and other fruit)* | | | | | | | | |
| Berries/pomegranate | | | | | | | | |
| Other fruit | | | | | | | | |
| Dried fruit | | | | | | | | |
| **NUTS AND SEEDS** | | | | | | | | |
| High omega-3: walnuts, chia, hemp, flax | | | | | | | | |
| Other nuts and seeds, avocado | | | | | | | | |
| **LIMITED FOODS** | | | | | | | | |
| Whole grains/starchy vegetables | | | | | | | | |
| Poultry, eggs, dairy, and fish | | | | | | | | |
| Oils | | | | | | | | |
| White potatoes | | | | | | | | |
| Added sodium | | | | | | | | |
| **FOODS TO AVOID** | | | | | | | | |
| Red meats | | | | | | | | |
| Sugar and sweets | | | | | | | | |
| White rice, white flour products, and processed foods | | | | | | | | |
| **SUPPLEMENTS — *Which supplements did I take today?*** | | | | | | | | |
| Multivitamin (no vitamins A or E, beta-carotene, folic acid, copper) | | | | | | | | |
| Vitamin D | | | | | | | | |
| Omega-3 fatty acids | | | | | | | | |
| Other | | | | | | | | |
| **EXERCISE — *How much did I exercise today?*** | | | | | | | | |
| Easy to moderate activity | | | | | | | | |
| Vigorous activity | | | | | | | | |

**TOTAL SCORE:**

# WEEKLY CALENDAR

**DID I MEET EACH OF MY GOALS TODAY?**

| | MON | TUE | WED | THU | FRI | SAT | SUN | MY WEEKLY SUPER IMMUNITY SCORE |
|---|---|---|---|---|---|---|---|---|
| **GREENS** (and other vegetables) | | | | | | | | |
| Raw leafy greens | | | | | | | | |
| Other raw vegetables | | | | | | | | |
| Total cooked vegetables | | | | | | | | |
| Cruciferous vegetables | | | | | | | | |
| Fresh vegetable juice | | | | | | | | |
| **BEANS** | | | | | | | | |
| Total beans and lentils | | | | | | | | |
| **ONIONS** | | | | | | | | |
| Vegetables from the onion family | | | | | | | | |
| **MUSHROOMS** | | | | | | | | |
| Cooked mushrooms | | | | | | | | |
| **BERRIES** (and other fruit) | | | | | | | | |
| Berries/pomegranate | | | | | | | | |
| Other fruit | | | | | | | | |
| Dried fruit | | | | | | | | |
| **NUTS AND SEEDS** | | | | | | | | |
| High omega-3: walnuts, chia, hemp, flax | | | | | | | | |
| Other nuts and seeds, avocado | | | | | | | | |
| **LIMITED FOODS** | | | | | | | | |
| Whole grains/starchy vegetables | | | | | | | | |
| Poultry, eggs, dairy, and fish | | | | | | | | |
| Oils | | | | | | | | |
| White potatoes | | | | | | | | |
| Added sodium | | | | | | | | |
| **FOODS TO AVOID** | | | | | | | | |
| Red meats | | | | | | | | |
| Sugar and sweets | | | | | | | | |
| White rice, white flour products, and processed foods | | | | | | | | |
| **SUPPLEMENTS — Which supplements did I take today?** | | | | | | | | |
| Multivitamin (no vitamins A or E, beta-carotene, folic acid, copper) | | | | | | | | |
| Vitamin D | | | | | | | | |
| Omega-3 fatty acids | | | | | | | | |
| Other | | | | | | | | |
| **EXERCISE — How much did I exercise today?** | | | | | | | | |
| Easy to moderate activity | | | | | | | | |
| Vigorous activity | | | | | | | | |

**TOTAL SCORE:**

## WEEKLY CALENDAR

### DID I MEET EACH OF MY GOALS TODAY?

| | MON | TUE | WED | THU | FRI | SAT | SUN | MY WEEKLY SUPER IMMUNITY SCORE |
|---|---|---|---|---|---|---|---|---|
| **GREENS** (and other vegetables) | | | | | | | | |
| Raw leafy greens | | | | | | | | |
| Other raw vegetables | | | | | | | | |
| Total cooked vegetables | | | | | | | | |
| Cruciferous vegetables | | | | | | | | |
| Fresh vegetable juice | | | | | | | | |
| **BEANS** | | | | | | | | |
| Total beans and lentils | | | | | | | | |
| **ONIONS** | | | | | | | | |
| Vegetables from the onion family | | | | | | | | |
| **MUSHROOMS** | | | | | | | | |
| Cooked mushrooms | | | | | | | | |
| **BERRIES** (and other fruit) | | | | | | | | |
| Berries/pomegranate | | | | | | | | |
| Other fruit | | | | | | | | |
| Dried fruit | | | | | | | | |
| **NUTS AND SEEDS** | | | | | | | | |
| High omega-3: walnuts, chia, hemp, flax | | | | | | | | |
| Other nuts and seeds, avocado | | | | | | | | |
| **LIMITED FOODS** | | | | | | | | |
| Whole grains/starchy vegetables | | | | | | | | |
| Poultry, eggs, dairy, and fish | | | | | | | | |
| Oils | | | | | | | | |
| White potatoes | | | | | | | | |
| Added sodium | | | | | | | | |
| **FOODS TO AVOID** | | | | | | | | |
| Red meats | | | | | | | | |
| Sugar and sweets | | | | | | | | |
| White rice, white flour products, and processed foods | | | | | | | | |
| **SUPPLEMENTS — Which supplements did I take today?** | | | | | | | | |
| Multivitamin (no vitamins A or E, beta-carotene, folic acid, copper) | | | | | | | | |
| Vitamin D | | | | | | | | |
| Omega-3 fatty acids | | | | | | | | |
| Other | | | | | | | | |
| **EXERCISE — How much did I exercise today?** | | | | | | | | |
| Easy to moderate activity | | | | | | | | |
| Vigorous activity | | | | | | | | |

**TOTAL SCORE:**

## WEEKLY CALENDAR

**DID I MEET EACH OF MY GOALS TODAY?**

| | MON | TUE | WED | THU | FRI | SAT | SUN | MY WEEKLY SUPER IMMUNITY SCORE |
|---|---|---|---|---|---|---|---|---|
| **GREENS** (*and other vegetables*) | | | | | | | | |
| Raw leafy greens | | | | | | | | |
| Other raw vegetables | | | | | | | | |
| Total cooked vegetables | | | | | | | | |
| Cruciferous vegetables | | | | | | | | |
| Fresh vegetable juice | | | | | | | | |
| **BEANS** | | | | | | | | |
| Total beans and lentils | | | | | | | | |
| **ONIONS** | | | | | | | | |
| Vegetables from the onion family | | | | | | | | |
| **MUSHROOMS** | | | | | | | | |
| Cooked mushrooms | | | | | | | | |
| **BERRIES** (*and other fruit*) | | | | | | | | |
| Berries/pomegranate | | | | | | | | |
| Other fruit | | | | | | | | |
| Dried fruit | | | | | | | | |
| **NUTS AND SEEDS** | | | | | | | | |
| High omega-3: walnuts, chia, hemp, flax | | | | | | | | |
| Other nuts and seeds, avocado | | | | | | | | |
| **LIMITED FOODS** | | | | | | | | |
| Whole grains/starchy vegetables | | | | | | | | |
| Poultry, eggs, dairy, and fish | | | | | | | | |
| Oils | | | | | | | | |
| White potatoes | | | | | | | | |
| Added sodium | | | | | | | | |
| **FOODS TO AVOID** | | | | | | | | |
| Red meats | | | | | | | | |
| Sugar and sweets | | | | | | | | |
| White rice, white flour products, and processed foods | | | | | | | | |
| **SUPPLEMENTS** — *Which supplements did I take today?* | | | | | | | | |
| Multivitamin (no vitamins A or E, beta-carotene, folic acid, copper) | | | | | | | | |
| Vitamin D | | | | | | | | |
| Omega-3 fatty acids | | | | | | | | |
| Other | | | | | | | | |
| **EXERCISE** — *How much did I exercise today?* | | | | | | | | |
| Easy to moderate activity | | | | | | | | |
| Vigorous activity | | | | | | | | |

**TOTAL SCORE:**

## WEEKLY CALENDAR

**DID I MEET EACH OF MY GOALS TODAY?**

| | MON | TUE | WED | THU | FRI | SAT | SUN | MY WEEKLY SUPER IMMUNITY SCORE |
|---|---|---|---|---|---|---|---|---|
| **GREENS** (and other vegetables) | | | | | | | | |
| Raw leafy greens | | | | | | | | |
| Other raw vegetables | | | | | | | | |
| Total cooked vegetables | | | | | | | | |
| Cruciferous vegetables | | | | | | | | |
| Fresh vegetable juice | | | | | | | | |
| **BEANS** | | | | | | | | |
| Total beans and lentils | | | | | | | | |
| **ONIONS** | | | | | | | | |
| Vegetables from the onion family | | | | | | | | |
| **MUSHROOMS** | | | | | | | | |
| Cooked mushrooms | | | | | | | | |
| **BERRIES** (and other fruit) | | | | | | | | |
| Berries/pomegranate | | | | | | | | |
| Other fruit | | | | | | | | |
| Dried fruit | | | | | | | | |
| **NUTS AND SEEDS** | | | | | | | | |
| High omega-3: walnuts, chia, hemp, flax | | | | | | | | |
| Other nuts and seeds, avocado | | | | | | | | |
| **LIMITED FOODS** | | | | | | | | |
| Whole grains/starchy vegetables | | | | | | | | |
| Poultry, eggs, dairy, and fish | | | | | | | | |
| Oils | | | | | | | | |
| White potatoes | | | | | | | | |
| Added sodium | | | | | | | | |
| **FOODS TO AVOID** | | | | | | | | |
| Red meats | | | | | | | | |
| Sugar and sweets | | | | | | | | |
| White rice, white flour products, and processed foods | | | | | | | | |
| **SUPPLEMENTS — Which supplements did I take today?** | | | | | | | | |
| Multivitamin (no vitamins A or E, beta-carotene, folic acid, copper) | | | | | | | | |
| Vitamin D | | | | | | | | |
| Omega-3 fatty acids | | | | | | | | |
| Other | | | | | | | | |
| **EXERCISE — How much did I exercise today?** | | | | | | | | |
| Easy to moderate activity | | | | | | | | |
| Vigorous activity | | | | | | | | |

**TOTAL SCORE:**

## WEEKLY CALENDAR

**DID I MEET EACH OF MY GOALS TODAY?**

| | MON | TUE | WED | THU | FRI | SAT | SUN | MY WEEKLY SUPER IMMUNITY SCORE |
|---|---|---|---|---|---|---|---|---|
| **GREENS** *(and other vegetables)* | | | | | | | | |
| Raw leafy greens | | | | | | | | |
| Other raw vegetables | | | | | | | | |
| Total cooked vegetables | | | | | | | | |
| Cruciferous vegetables | | | | | | | | |
| Fresh vegetable juice | | | | | | | | |
| **BEANS** | | | | | | | | |
| Total beans and lentils | | | | | | | | |
| **ONIONS** | | | | | | | | |
| Vegetables from the onion family | | | | | | | | |
| **MUSHROOMS** | | | | | | | | |
| Cooked mushrooms | | | | | | | | |
| **BERRIES** *(and other fruit)* | | | | | | | | |
| Berries/pomegranate | | | | | | | | |
| Other fruit | | | | | | | | |
| Dried fruit | | | | | | | | |
| **NUTS AND SEEDS** | | | | | | | | |
| High omega-3: walnuts, chia, hemp, flax | | | | | | | | |
| Other nuts and seeds, avocado | | | | | | | | |
| **LIMITED FOODS** | | | | | | | | |
| Whole grains/starchy vegetables | | | | | | | | |
| Poultry, eggs, dairy, and fish | | | | | | | | |
| Oils | | | | | | | | |
| White potatoes | | | | | | | | |
| Added sodium | | | | | | | | |
| **FOODS TO AVOID** | | | | | | | | |
| Red meats | | | | | | | | |
| Sugar and sweets | | | | | | | | |
| White rice, white flour products, and processed foods | | | | | | | | |
| **SUPPLEMENTS** — *Which supplements did I take today?* | | | | | | | | |
| Multivitamin (no vitamins A or E, beta-carotene, folic acid, copper) | | | | | | | | |
| Vitamin D | | | | | | | | |
| Omega-3 fatty acids | | | | | | | | |
| Other | | | | | | | | |
| **EXERCISE** — *How much did I exercise today?* | | | | | | | | |
| Easy to moderate activity | | | | | | | | |
| Vigorous activity | | | | | | | | |

**TOTAL SCORE:**

## WEEKLY CALENDAR

**DID I MEET EACH OF MY GOALS TODAY?**

| | MON | TUE | WED | THU | FRI | SAT | SUN | MY WEEKLY SUPER IMMUNITY SCORE |
|---|---|---|---|---|---|---|---|---|
| **GREENS** (and other vegetables) | | | | | | | | |
| Raw leafy greens | | | | | | | | |
| Other raw vegetables | | | | | | | | |
| Total cooked vegetables | | | | | | | | |
| Cruciferous vegetables | | | | | | | | |
| Fresh vegetable juice | | | | | | | | |
| **BEANS** | | | | | | | | |
| Total beans and lentils | | | | | | | | |
| **ONIONS** | | | | | | | | |
| Vegetables from the onion family | | | | | | | | |
| **MUSHROOMS** | | | | | | | | |
| Cooked mushrooms | | | | | | | | |
| **BERRIES** (and other fruit) | | | | | | | | |
| Berries/pomegranate | | | | | | | | |
| Other fruit | | | | | | | | |
| Dried fruit | | | | | | | | |
| **NUTS AND SEEDS** | | | | | | | | |
| High omega-3: walnuts, chia, hemp, flax | | | | | | | | |
| Other nuts and seeds, avocado | | | | | | | | |
| **LIMITED FOODS** | | | | | | | | |
| Whole grains/starchy vegetables | | | | | | | | |
| Poultry, eggs, dairy, and fish | | | | | | | | |
| Oils | | | | | | | | |
| White potatoes | | | | | | | | |
| Added sodium | | | | | | | | |
| **FOODS TO AVOID** | | | | | | | | |
| Red meats | | | | | | | | |
| Sugar and sweets | | | | | | | | |
| White rice, white flour products, and processed foods | | | | | | | | |
| **SUPPLEMENTS** — *Which supplements did I take today?* | | | | | | | | |
| Multivitamin (no vitamins A or E, beta-carotene, folic acid, copper) | | | | | | | | |
| Vitamin D | | | | | | | | |
| Omega-3 fatty acids | | | | | | | | |
| Other | | | | | | | | |
| **EXERCISE** — *How much did I exercise today?* | | | | | | | | |
| Easy to moderate activity | | | | | | | | |
| Vigorous activity | | | | | | | | |

**TOTAL SCORE:**

# WEEKLY CALENDAR

**DID I MEET EACH OF MY GOALS TODAY?**

| | MON | TUE | WED | THU | FRI | SAT | SUN | MY WEEKLY SUPER IMMUNITY SCORE |
|---|---|---|---|---|---|---|---|---|
| **GREENS** (*and other vegetables*) | | | | | | | | |
| Raw leafy greens | | | | | | | | |
| Other raw vegetables | | | | | | | | |
| Total cooked vegetables | | | | | | | | |
| Cruciferous vegetables | | | | | | | | |
| Fresh vegetable juice | | | | | | | | |
| **BEANS** | | | | | | | | |
| Total beans and lentils | | | | | | | | |
| **ONIONS** | | | | | | | | |
| Vegetables from the onion family | | | | | | | | |
| **MUSHROOMS** | | | | | | | | |
| Cooked mushrooms | | | | | | | | |
| **BERRIES** (*and other fruit*) | | | | | | | | |
| Berries/pomegranate | | | | | | | | |
| Other fruit | | | | | | | | |
| Dried fruit | | | | | | | | |
| **NUTS AND SEEDS** | | | | | | | | |
| High omega-3: walnuts, chia, hemp, flax | | | | | | | | |
| Other nuts and seeds, avocado | | | | | | | | |
| **LIMITED FOODS** | | | | | | | | |
| Whole grains/starchy vegetables | | | | | | | | |
| Poultry, eggs, dairy, and fish | | | | | | | | |
| Oils | | | | | | | | |
| White potatoes | | | | | | | | |
| Added sodium | | | | | | | | |
| **FOODS TO AVOID** | | | | | | | | |
| Red meats | | | | | | | | |
| Sugar and sweets | | | | | | | | |
| White rice, white flour products, and processed foods | | | | | | | | |
| **SUPPLEMENTS** — *Which supplements did I take today?* | | | | | | | | |
| Multivitamin (no vitamins A or E, beta-carotene, folic acid, copper) | | | | | | | | |
| Vitamin D | | | | | | | | |
| Omega-3 fatty acids | | | | | | | | |
| Other | | | | | | | | |
| **EXERCISE** — *How much did I exercise today?* | | | | | | | | |
| Easy to moderate activity | | | | | | | | |
| Vigorous activity | | | | | | | | |

**TOTAL SCORE:**

WEEKLY CALENDAR

DID I MEET EACH OF MY GOALS TODAY?

| | MON | TUE | WED | THU | FRI | SAT | SUN | MY WEEKLY SUPER IMMUNITY SCORE |
|---|---|---|---|---|---|---|---|---|
| **GREENS** *(and other vegetables)* | | | | | | | | |
| Raw leafy greens | | | | | | | | |
| Other raw vegetables | | | | | | | | |
| Total cooked vegetables | | | | | | | | |
| Cruciferous vegetables | | | | | | | | |
| Fresh vegetable juice | | | | | | | | |
| **BEANS** | | | | | | | | |
| Total beans and lentils | | | | | | | | |
| **ONIONS** | | | | | | | | |
| Vegetables from the onion family | | | | | | | | |
| **MUSHROOMS** | | | | | | | | |
| Cooked mushrooms | | | | | | | | |
| **BERRIES** *(and other fruit)* | | | | | | | | |
| Berries/pomegranate | | | | | | | | |
| Other fruit | | | | | | | | |
| Dried fruit | | | | | | | | |
| **NUTS AND SEEDS** | | | | | | | | |
| High omega-3: walnuts, chia, hemp, flax | | | | | | | | |
| Other nuts and seeds, avocado | | | | | | | | |
| **LIMITED FOODS** | | | | | | | | |
| Whole grains/starchy vegetables | | | | | | | | |
| Poultry, eggs, dairy, and fish | | | | | | | | |
| Oils | | | | | | | | |
| White potatoes | | | | | | | | |
| Added sodium | | | | | | | | |
| **FOODS TO AVOID** | | | | | | | | |
| Red meats | | | | | | | | |
| Sugar and sweets | | | | | | | | |
| White rice, white flour products, and processed foods | | | | | | | | |
| **SUPPLEMENTS — *Which supplements did I take today?*** | | | | | | | | |
| Multivitamin (no vitamins A or E, beta-carotene, folic acid, copper) | | | | | | | | |
| Vitamin D | | | | | | | | |
| Omega-3 fatty acids | | | | | | | | |
| Other | | | | | | | | |
| **EXERCISE — *How much did I exercise today?*** | | | | | | | | |
| Easy to moderate activity | | | | | | | | |
| Vigorous activity | | | | | | | | |

**TOTAL SCORE:**

**DID I MEET EACH OF MY GOALS TODAY?**

| | MON | TUE | WED | THU | FRI | SAT | SUN | MY WEEKLY SUPER IMMUNITY SCORE |
|---|---|---|---|---|---|---|---|---|
| **GREENS** (*and other vegetables*) | | | | | | | | |
| Raw leafy greens | | | | | | | | |
| Other raw vegetables | | | | | | | | |
| Total cooked vegetables | | | | | | | | |
| Cruciferous vegetables | | | | | | | | |
| Fresh vegetable juice | | | | | | | | |
| **BEANS** | | | | | | | | |
| Total beans and lentils | | | | | | | | |
| **ONIONS** | | | | | | | | |
| Vegetables from the onion family | | | | | | | | |
| **MUSHROOMS** | | | | | | | | |
| Cooked mushrooms | | | | | | | | |
| **BERRIES** (*and other fruit*) | | | | | | | | |
| Berries/pomegranate | | | | | | | | |
| Other fruit | | | | | | | | |
| Dried fruit | | | | | | | | |
| **NUTS AND SEEDS** | | | | | | | | |
| High omega-3: walnuts, chia, hemp, flax | | | | | | | | |
| Other nuts and seeds, avocado | | | | | | | | |
| **LIMITED FOODS** | | | | | | | | |
| Whole grains/starchy vegetables | | | | | | | | |
| Poultry, eggs, dairy, and fish | | | | | | | | |
| Oils | | | | | | | | |
| White potatoes | | | | | | | | |
| Added sodium | | | | | | | | |
| **FOODS TO AVOID** | | | | | | | | |
| Red meats | | | | | | | | |
| Sugar and sweets | | | | | | | | |
| White rice, white flour products, and processed foods | | | | | | | | |
| **SUPPLEMENTS — *Which supplements did I take today?*** | | | | | | | | |
| Multivitamin (no vitamins A or E, beta-carotene, folic acid, copper) | | | | | | | | |
| Vitamin D | | | | | | | | |
| Omega-3 fatty acids | | | | | | | | |
| Other | | | | | | | | |
| **EXERCISE — *How much did I exercise today?*** | | | | | | | | |
| Easy to moderate activity | | | | | | | | |
| Vigorous activity | | | | | | | | |

**TOTAL SCORE:**

## WEEKLY CALENDAR

**DID I MEET EACH OF MY GOALS TODAY?**

| | MON | TUE | WED | THU | FRI | SAT | SUN | MY WEEKLY SUPER IMMUNITY SCORE |
|---|---|---|---|---|---|---|---|---|
| **GREENS** *(and other vegetables)* | | | | | | | | |
| Raw leafy greens | | | | | | | | |
| Other raw vegetables | | | | | | | | |
| Total cooked vegetables | | | | | | | | |
| Cruciferous vegetables | | | | | | | | |
| Fresh vegetable juice | | | | | | | | |
| **BEANS** | | | | | | | | |
| Total beans and lentils | | | | | | | | |
| **ONIONS** | | | | | | | | |
| Vegetables from the onion family | | | | | | | | |
| **MUSHROOMS** | | | | | | | | |
| Cooked mushrooms | | | | | | | | |
| **BERRIES** *(and other fruit)* | | | | | | | | |
| Berries/pomegranate | | | | | | | | |
| Other fruit | | | | | | | | |
| Dried fruit | | | | | | | | |
| **NUTS AND SEEDS** | | | | | | | | |
| High omega-3: walnuts, chia, hemp, flax | | | | | | | | |
| Other nuts and seeds, avocado | | | | | | | | |
| **LIMITED FOODS** | | | | | | | | |
| Whole grains/starchy vegetables | | | | | | | | |
| Poultry, eggs, dairy, and fish | | | | | | | | |
| Oils | | | | | | | | |
| White potatoes | | | | | | | | |
| Added sodium | | | | | | | | |
| **FOODS TO AVOID** | | | | | | | | |
| Red meats | | | | | | | | |
| Sugar and sweets | | | | | | | | |
| White rice, white flour products, and processed foods | | | | | | | | |
| **SUPPLEMENTS — *Which supplements did I take today?*** | | | | | | | | |
| Multivitamin (no vitamins A or E, beta-carotene, folic acid, copper) | | | | | | | | |
| Vitamin D | | | | | | | | |
| Omega-3 fatty acids | | | | | | | | |
| Other | | | | | | | | |
| **EXERCISE — *How much did I exercise today?*** | | | | | | | | |
| Easy to moderate activity | | | | | | | | |
| Vigorous activity | | | | | | | | |

**TOTAL SCORE:**

# WEEKLY CALENDAR

**DID I MEET EACH OF MY GOALS TODAY?**

| | MON | TUE | WED | THU | FRI | SAT | SUN | MY WEEKLY SUPER IMMUNITY SCORE |
|---|---|---|---|---|---|---|---|---|
| **GREENS** *(and other vegetables)* | | | | | | | | |
| Raw leafy greens | | | | | | | | |
| Other raw vegetables | | | | | | | | |
| Total cooked vegetables | | | | | | | | |
| Cruciferous vegetables | | | | | | | | |
| Fresh vegetable juice | | | | | | | | |
| **BEANS** | | | | | | | | |
| Total beans and lentils | | | | | | | | |
| **ONIONS** | | | | | | | | |
| Vegetables from the onion family | | | | | | | | |
| **MUSHROOMS** | | | | | | | | |
| Cooked mushrooms | | | | | | | | |
| **BERRIES** *(and other fruit)* | | | | | | | | |
| Berries/pomegranate | | | | | | | | |
| Other fruit | | | | | | | | |
| Dried fruit | | | | | | | | |
| **NUTS AND SEEDS** | | | | | | | | |
| High omega-3: walnuts, chia, hemp, flax | | | | | | | | |
| Other nuts and seeds, avocado | | | | | | | | |
| **LIMITED FOODS** | | | | | | | | |
| Whole grains/starchy vegetables | | | | | | | | |
| Poultry, eggs, dairy, and fish | | | | | | | | |
| Oils | | | | | | | | |
| White potatoes | | | | | | | | |
| Added sodium | | | | | | | | |
| **FOODS TO AVOID** | | | | | | | | |
| Red meats | | | | | | | | |
| Sugar and sweets | | | | | | | | |
| White rice, white flour products, and processed foods | | | | | | | | |
| **SUPPLEMENTS** — *Which supplements did I take today?* | | | | | | | | |
| Multivitamin (no vitamins A or E, beta-carotene, folic acid, copper) | | | | | | | | |
| Vitamin D | | | | | | | | |
| Omega-3 fatty acids | | | | | | | | |
| Other | | | | | | | | |
| **EXERCISE** — *How much did I exercise today?* | | | | | | | | |
| Easy to moderate activity | | | | | | | | |
| Vigorous activity | | | | | | | | |

**TOTAL SCORE:**

**DID I MEET EACH OF MY GOALS TODAY?**

| | MON | TUE | WED | THU | FRI | SAT | SUN | MY WEEKLY SUPER IMMUNITY SCORE |
|---|---|---|---|---|---|---|---|---|
| **GREENS** (*and other vegetables*) | | | | | | | | |
| Raw leafy greens | | | | | | | | |
| Other raw vegetables | | | | | | | | |
| Total cooked vegetables | | | | | | | | |
| Cruciferous vegetables | | | | | | | | |
| Fresh vegetable juice | | | | | | | | |
| **BEANS** | | | | | | | | |
| Total beans and lentils | | | | | | | | |
| **ONIONS** | | | | | | | | |
| Vegetables from the onion family | | | | | | | | |
| **MUSHROOMS** | | | | | | | | |
| Cooked mushrooms | | | | | | | | |
| **BERRIES** (*and other fruit*) | | | | | | | | |
| Berries/pomegranate | | | | | | | | |
| Other fruit | | | | | | | | |
| Dried fruit | | | | | | | | |
| **NUTS AND SEEDS** | | | | | | | | |
| High omega-3: walnuts, chia, hemp, flax | | | | | | | | |
| Other nuts and seeds, avocado | | | | | | | | |
| **LIMITED FOODS** | | | | | | | | |
| Whole grains/starchy vegetables | | | | | | | | |
| Poultry, eggs, dairy, and fish | | | | | | | | |
| Oils | | | | | | | | |
| White potatoes | | | | | | | | |
| Added sodium | | | | | | | | |
| **FOODS TO AVOID** | | | | | | | | |
| Red meats | | | | | | | | |
| Sugar and sweets | | | | | | | | |
| White rice, white flour products, and processed foods | | | | | | | | |
| **SUPPLEMENTS** — *Which supplements did I take today?* | | | | | | | | |
| Multivitamin (no vitamins A or E, beta-carotene, folic acid, copper) | | | | | | | | |
| Vitamin D | | | | | | | | |
| Omega-3 fatty acids | | | | | | | | |
| Other | | | | | | | | |
| **EXERCISE** — *How much did I exercise today?* | | | | | | | | |
| Easy to moderate activity | | | | | | | | |
| Vigorous activity | | | | | | | | |

**TOTAL SCORE:**

## WEEKLY CALENDAR

**DID I MEET EACH OF MY GOALS TODAY?**

| | MON | TUE | WED | THU | FRI | SAT | SUN | MY WEEKLY SUPER IMMUNITY SCORE |
|---|---|---|---|---|---|---|---|---|
| **GREENS** (and other vegetables) | | | | | | | | |
| Raw leafy greens | | | | | | | | |
| Other raw vegetables | | | | | | | | |
| Total cooked vegetables | | | | | | | | |
| Cruciferous vegetables | | | | | | | | |
| Fresh vegetable juice | | | | | | | | |
| **BEANS** | | | | | | | | |
| Total beans and lentils | | | | | | | | |
| **ONIONS** | | | | | | | | |
| Vegetables from the onion family | | | | | | | | |
| **MUSHROOMS** | | | | | | | | |
| Cooked mushrooms | | | | | | | | |
| **BERRIES** (and other fruit) | | | | | | | | |
| Berries/pomegranate | | | | | | | | |
| Other fruit | | | | | | | | |
| Dried fruit | | | | | | | | |
| **NUTS AND SEEDS** | | | | | | | | |
| High omega-3: walnuts, chia, hemp, flax | | | | | | | | |
| Other nuts and seeds, avocado | | | | | | | | |
| **LIMITED FOODS** | | | | | | | | |
| Whole grains/starchy vegetables | | | | | | | | |
| Poultry, eggs, dairy, and fish | | | | | | | | |
| Oils | | | | | | | | |
| White potatoes | | | | | | | | |
| Added sodium | | | | | | | | |
| **FOODS TO AVOID** | | | | | | | | |
| Red meats | | | | | | | | |
| Sugar and sweets | | | | | | | | |
| White rice, white flour products, and processed foods | | | | | | | | |
| **SUPPLEMENTS — Which supplements did I take today?** | | | | | | | | |
| Multivitamin (no vitamins A or E, beta-carotene, folic acid, copper) | | | | | | | | |
| Vitamin D | | | | | | | | |
| Omega-3 fatty acids | | | | | | | | |
| Other | | | | | | | | |
| **EXERCISE — How much did I exercise today?** | | | | | | | | |
| Easy to moderate activity | | | | | | | | |
| Vigorous activity | | | | | | | | |

**TOTAL SCORE:**

1. Deaths: Preliminary Data for 2010. In Natl Vital Stat Rep, vol. 60. pp. 42 (Major Cardiovascular Diseases): U.S. Centers for Disease Control and Prevention; 2012:42 (Major Cardiovascular Diseases).

2. National Intelligence Estimate. The Global Infectious Disease Threat and Its Implications for the United States. http://www.dni.gov/nic/PDF_GIF_otherprod/infectiousdisease/infectious-diseases.pdf

3. U.S. Department of Agriculture Economic Research Service. http://www.ers.usda.gov/Data/FoodConsumption/FoodGuideSpreadsheets.htm#calories

4. Carter P, Gray LJ, Troughton J, et al. Fruit and vegetable intake and incidence of type 2 diabetes mellitus: systematic review and meta-analysis. BMJ. 2010 Aug 18;341:c4229.
Journal of Clinical Investigation (2011, March 24). High levels of dietary nitrate might in part explain the vascular benefits of diets rich in leafy greens. ScienceDaily. Retrieved March 30, 2011, from http://www.sciencedaily.com /releases/2011/03/110323135631.htm

5. Stringham JM, Bovier ER, Wong JC, Hammond BR Jr. The influence of dietary lutein and zeaxanthin on visual performance. J Food Sci. 2010 Jan-Feb;75(1):R24-9.

6. Higdon JV, Delage B, Williams DE, Dashwood RH. Cruciferous vegetables and human cancer risk: epidemiologic evidence and mechanistic basis. Pharmacol Res. 2007 Mar;55(3):224-36.
Cavell BE, Syed Alwi SS, Donlevy A, et al., Anti-angiogenic effects of dietary isothiocyanates: mechanisms of action and implications for human health. Biochem. Pharmacol., 2011. 81(3): p. 327-36.

7. Xue L, Pestka JJ, Li M, et al. 3,3'-Diindolylmethane stimulates murine immune function in vitro and in vivo. J Nutr Biochem. 2008 May;19(5):336-44.

8. Zeligs MA, Sepkovic DW, Manrique C, et al. Absorption-enhanced 3,3-Diindolylmethane: human use in HPV-related, benign and precancerous conditions. Proc Am Assoc Cancer Res 2003; 44: 3198

9. Conrad A, Bauer D, Nobis T, et al. In vitro activity of a mixture of mustard oils (isothiocyanates) against antimicrobial and multidrug-resistant bacteria. 18th European Congress of Clinical Microbiology and Infectious Diseases 2008, Ap 19; Barcelona, Spain. Abstract number: P614

10. Fahey JW, Haristoy X, Dolan PM, et al. Sulforaphane inhibits extracellular, intracellular, and antibiotic-resistant strains of Helicobacter pylori and prevents benzo[a]pyrene-induced stomach tumors. Proc Natl Acad Sci U S A. 2002 May 28;99(11):7610-5.
Haristoy X, Angioi-Duprez K, Duprez A, Lozniewski A. Efficacy of sulforaphane in eradicating Helicobacter pylori in human gastric xenografts implanted in nude mice. Antimicrob Agents Chemother. 2003 Dec;47(12):3982-4.
Galan MV, Kishan AA, Silverman AL. Oral broccoli sprouts for the treatment of Helicobacter pylori infection: a preliminary report. Dig Dis Sci. 2004 Aug;49(7-8):1088-90.

11. Li Y, Innocentin S, Withers DR, et al. Exogenous Stimuli Maintain Intraepithelial Lymphocytes via  Aryl Hydrocarbon Receptor Activation. Cell. 2011 Oct 28;147(3):629-40.

12. Bazzano LA, Thompson AM, Tees MT, et al. Non-soy legume consumption lowers cholesterol levels: A meta-analysis of randomized controlled trials. Nutr Metab Cardiovasc Dis 2011 Feb;21(2):94-103.

13. O'Keefe SJ, Ou J, Aufreiter S, et al. Products of the colonic microbiota mediate the effects of diet on colon cancer risk. J Nutr. 2009 Nov;139(11):2044-8.
Aune D, De Stefani E, Ronco A, et al. Legume intake and the risk of cancer: a multisite case-control study in Uruguay. Cancer Causes Control. 2009 Nov;20(9):1605-15.

14. Singh PN, Fraser GE. Dietary risk factors for colon cancer in a low-risk population. Am J Epidemiol. 1998 Oct 15;148(8):761-74.

15. Aune D, De Stefani E, Ronco A, et al. Legume intake and the risk of cancer: a multisite case-control study in Uruguay. Cancer Causes Control. 2009 Nov;20(9):1605-15.

16. Bednar GE, Patil AR, Murray SM et al. Starch and fiber fractions in selected food and feed ingredients affect their small intestinal digestibility and fermentability and their large bowel fermentability in vitro in a canine model. J Nutr. 2001;131(2): 276-86
Muir J, O' Dea K. Measurement of Resistant Starch: factors affecting the amount of starch escaping digestion in vitro. Am J Clin Nutr 1992;56:123-7.
Atkinson FS, Foster-Powell K, Brand-Miller JC. International tables of glycemic index and glycemic load values: 2008. Diabetes Care. 2008 Dec;31(12):2281-3.
Foster-Powell K, Holt SH, Brand-Miller JC. International table of glycemic index and glycemic load values: 2002. Am J Clin Nutr. 2002 Jul;76(1):5-56. index and glycemic load values: 2002. Am J Clin Nutr. 2002 Jul;76(1):5-56.

17. Powolny AA, Singh SV. Multitargeted prevention and therapy of cancer by diallyl trisulfide and related Allium vegetable-derived organosulfur compounds. Cancer Lett. 2008 Oct 8;269(2):305-14.

18. Galeone C, Pelucchi C, Levi F, et al. Onion and garlic use and human cancer. Am J Clin Nutr. 2006 Nov;84(5):1027-32.

19. Pierini R, Gee JM, Belshaw NJ, et al. Flavonoids and intestinal cancers. Br J Nutr. 2008 May;99 E Suppl 1:ES53-9.
Slimestad R, Fossen T, Vågen IM. Onions: a source of unique dietary flavonoids. J Agric Food Chem. 2007 Dec 12;55(25):10067-80.

20. Miyamoto S, Yasui Y, Ohigashi H, et al. Dietary flavonoids suppress azoxymethane-induced colonic preneoplastic lesions in male C57BL/KsJ-db/db mice. Chem Biol Interact. 2010 Jan 27;183(2):276-83.
Shan BE, Wang MX, Li RQ. Quercetin inhibit human SW480 colon cancer growth in association with inhibition of cyclin D1 and survivin expression through Wnt/beta-catenin signaling pathway. Cancer Invest. 2009 Jul;27(6):604-12.
Xavier CP, Lima CF, Preto A, et al. Luteolin, quercetin and ursolic acid are potent inhibitors of proliferation and inducers of apoptosis in both KRAS and BRAF mutated human colorectal cancer cells. Cancer Lett. 2009 Aug 28;281(2):162-70.

21. Ravasco P, Aranha MM, Borralho PM, et al. Colorectal cancer: Can nutrients modulate NF-kappaB and apoptosis? Clin Nutr. 2010 Feb;29(1):42-46.

22. Borchers AT, Keen CL, Gershwin ME. Mushrooms, tumors, and immunity: an update. Exp Biol Med 2004;229:393-406.
    Borchers AT, Krishnamurthy A, Keen CL, et al. The Immunobiology of Mushrooms. Exp Biol Med 2008;233:259-276.

23. Yu L, Fernig DG, Smith JA, et al. Reversible inhibition of proliferation of epithelial cell lines by Agaricus bisporus (edible mushroom) lectin. Cancer Res 1993;53:4627-4632.
    Carrizo ME, Capaldi S, Perduca M, et al. The antineoplastic lectin of the common edible mushroom (Agaricus bisporus) has two binding sites, each specific for a different configuration at a single epimeric hydroxyl. The Journal of biological chemistry 2005;280:10614-10623.

24. Kohno K, Miyake M, Sano O, et al. Anti-inflammatory and immunomodulatory properties of 2-amino-3H-phenoxazin-3-one. Biol Pharm Bull 2008;31:1938-1945.
    Lee JS, Park SY, Thapa D, et al. Grifola frondosa water extract alleviates intestinal inflammation by suppressing TNF-alpha production and its signaling. Exp Mol Med 2010;42:143-154.

25. Hara M, Hanaoka T, Kobayashi M, et al. Cruciferous vegetables, mushrooms, and gastrointestinal cancer risks in a multicenter, hospital-based case-control study in Japan. Nutr Cancer 2003;46:138-147.

26. Hong SA, Kim K, Nam SJ, et al. A case-control study on the dietary intake of mushrooms and breast cancer risk among Korean women. Int J Cancer 2008;122:919-923.
    Shin A, Kim J, Lim SY, et al. Dietary mushroom intake and the risk of breast cancer based on hormone receptor status. Nutr Cancer 2010;62:476-483.
    Zhang M, Huang J, Xie X, et al. Dietary intakes of mushrooms and green tea combine to reduce the risk of breast cancer in Chinese women. Int J Cancer 2009;124:1404-1408.

27. Martin KR, Brophy SK. Commonly consumed and specialty dietary mushrooms reduce cellular proliferation in MCF-7 human breast cancer cells. Exp Biol Med 2010;235:1306-1314.
    Fang N, Li Q, Yu S, et al. Inhibition of growth and induction of apoptosis in human cancer cell lines by an ethyl acetate fraction from shiitake mushrooms. J Altern Complement Med 2006;12:125-132.
    Ng ML, Yap AT. Inhibition of human colon carcinoma development by lentinan from shiitake mushrooms (Lentinus edodes). J Altern Complement Med 2002;8:581-589.
    Adams LS, Phung S, Wu X, et al. White button mushroom (Agaricus bisporus) exhibits antiproliferative and proapoptotic properties and inhibits prostate tumor growth in athymic mice. Nutr Cancer 2008;60:744-756.
    Lakshmi B, Ajith TA, Sheena N, et al. Antiperoxidative, anti-inflammatory, and antimutagenic activities of ethanol extract of the mycelium of Ganoderma lucidum occurring in South India. Teratog Carcinog Mutagen 2003;Suppl 1:85-97.
    Cao QZ, Lin ZB. Antitumor and anti-angiogenic activity of Ganoderma lucidum polysaccharides peptide. Acta pharmacologica Sinica 2004;25:833-838.
    Lin ZB, Zhang HN. Anti-tumor and immunoregulatory activities of Ganoderma lucidum and its possible mechanisms. Acta pharmacologica Sinica 2004;25:1387-1395.

28. Aviram M, Rosenblat M, Gaitini D, et al. Pomegranate juice consumption for 3 years by patients with carotid artery stenosis reduces common carotid intima-media thickness, blood pressure and LDL oxidation. Clin Nutr 2004;23:423-433.

Aviram M, Volkova N, Coleman R, et al. Pomegranate phenolics from the peels, arils, and flowers are antiatherogenic: studies in vivo in atherosclerotic apolipoprotein e-deficient (E 0) mice and in vitro in cultured macrophages and lipoproteins. J Ag Food Chem 2008;56:1148-1157.

29. Stoner GD, Wang LS, Casto BC. Laboratory and clinical studies of cancer chemoprevention by antioxidants in berries. Carcinogenesis. 2008 Sep;29(9):1665-74.

Roy S, Khanna S, Alessio HM, et al: Anti-angiogenic property of edible berries. Free Radic Res 2002, 36:1023-1031.

Hannum SM. Potential impact of strawberries on human health: a review of the science. Crit Rev Food Sci Nutr. 2004;44(1):1-17.

Cassidy A, O'Reilly EJ, Kay C, et al: Habitual intake of flavonoid subclasses and incident hypertension in adults. Am J Clin Nutr 2011, 93:338-347.

30. Bazzano LA, Li TY, Joshipura KJ, Hu FB. Intake of fruit, vegetables, and fruit juices and risk of diabetes in women. Diabetes Care. 2008 Jul;31(7):1311-7.

Joseph JA, Shukitt-Hale B, Willis LM. Grape juice, berries, and walnuts affect brain aging and behavior. J Nutr. 2009 Sep;139(9):1813S-7S.

Stoner GD, Wang LS, Casto BC. Laboratory and clinical studies of cancer chemoprevention by antioxidants in berries. Carcinogenesis. 2008 Sep;29(9):1665-74.

31. Bickford PC, Shukitt-Hale B, Joseph J. Effects of aging on cerebellar noradrenergic function and motor learning: nutritional interventions. Mech Ageing Dev. 1999 Nov;111(2-3):141-54.

Krikorian R, Shidler MD, Nash TA, et al. Blueberry supplementation improves memory in older adults. J Agric Food Chem. 2010 Apr 14;58(7):3996-4000.

32. Nash SD, Nash DT. Nuts as part of a healthy cardiovascular diet. Curr Atheroscler Rep. 2008 Dec;10(6):529-35.

Sabaté J, Ang Y. Nuts and health outcomes: new epidemiologic evidence. Am J Clin Nutr. 2009 May;89(5):1643S-1648S.

Mattes RD et al. Impact of peanuts and tree nuts on body weight and healthy weight loss in adults. J Nutr. 2008 Sep;138(9):1741S-1745S.

Natoli S, McCoy P. A review of the evidence: nuts and body weight. Asia Pac J Clin Nutr. 2007;16(4):588-97

Kendall CW, Josse AR, Esfahani A, Jenkins DJ. Nuts, metabolic syndrome and diabetes. Br J Nutr. 2010 Aug;104(4):465-73.

33. Bassett CM, Rodriguez-Leyva D, Pierce GN. Experimental and clinical research findings on the cardiovascular benefits of consuming flaxseed. Appl Physiol Nutr Metab. 2009 Oct;34(5):965-74.

Webb AL, McCullough ML. Dietary lignans: potential role in cancer prevention. Nutr Cancer. 2005;51(2):117-31.

Saarinen NM, Wärri A, Airio M, et al. Role of dietary lignans in the reduction of breast cancer risk. Mol Nutr Food Res. 2007 Jul;51(7):857-66.

Coulman KD, Liu Z, Hum WQ, et al. Whole sesame seed is as rich a source of mammalian lignan precursors as whole flaxseed. Nutr Cancer. 2005;52(2):156-65.

34. Shahidi F, Liyana-Pathirana CM, Wall DS. Antioxidant activity of white and black sesame seeds and their hull fractions. Food Chemistry 2006;99(3): 478-483.

35. Lee, J.S., B.C. Park, Y.J. Ko, et al., Grifola frondosa (maitake mushroom) water extract inhibits vascular endothelial growth factor-induced angiogenesis through inhibition of reactive oxygen species and extracellular signal-regulated kinase phosphorylation. J Med Food, 2008. 11(4): p. 643-51.

Chang, H.H., K.Y. Hsieh, C.H. Yeh, et al., Oral administration of an Enoki mushroom protein FVE activates innate and adaptive immunity and induces anti-tumor activity against murine hepatocellular carcinoma. International immunopharmacology, 2010. 10(2): p. 239-46.

Cao, Q.Z. and Z.B. Lin, Antitumor and anti-angiogenic activity of Ganoderma lucidum polysaccharides peptide. Acta pharmacologica Sinica, 2004. 25(6): p. 833-8.

Liu, M., R.H. Liu, B.B. Song, et al., Antiangiogenetic effects of 4 varieties of grapes in vitro. Journal of food science, 2010. 75(6): p. T99-104.

Kunimasa, K., M. Ikekita, M. Sato, et al., Nobiletin, a citrus polymethoxyflavonoid, suppresses multiple angiogenesis-related endothelial cell functions and angiogenesis in vivo. Cancer science, 2010. 101(11): p. 2462-9.

Ashino, H., M. Shimamura, H. Nakajima, et al., Novel function of ascorbic acid as an angiostatic factor. Angiogenesis, 2003. 6(4): p. 259-69.

Kenny, T.P., C.L. Keen, P. Jones, et al., Cocoa procyanidins inhibit proliferation and angiogenic signals in human dermal microvascular endothelial cells following stimulation by low-level H2O2. Exp. Biol. Med., 2004. 229(8): p. 765-71.

Kang, X., S. Jin, and Q. Zhang, Antitumor and antiangiogenic activity of soy phytoestrogen on 7,12-dimethylbenz[alpha]anthracene-induced mammary tumors following ovariectomy in Sprague-Dawley rats. Journal of food science, 2009. 74(7): p. H237-42.

Fotsis, T., M. Pepper, H. Adlercreutz, et al., Genistein, a dietary-derived inhibitor of in vitro angiogenesis. Proc. Natl. Acad. Sci. U. S. A., 1993. 90(7): p. 2690-4.

Bergman Jungestrom, M., L.U. Thompson, and C. Dabrosin, Flaxseed and its lignans inhibit estradiol-induced growth, angiogenesis, and secretion of vascular endothelial growth factor in human breast cancer xenografts in vivo. Clinical cancer research : an official journal of the American Association for Cancer Research, 2007. 13(3): p. 1061-7.

Khan, N., F. Afaq, M.H. Kweon, et al., Oral consumption of pomegranate fruit extract inhibits growth and progression of primary lung tumors in mice. Cancer Res., 2007. 67(7): p. 3475-82.

Toi, M., H. Bando, C. Ramachandran, et al., Preliminary studies on the anti-angiogenic potential of pomegranate fractions in vitro and in vivo. Angiogenesis, 2003. 6(2): p. 121-8.

Sartippour, M.R., N.P. Seeram, J.Y. Rao, et al., Ellagitannin-rich pomegranate extract inhibits angiogenesis in prostate cancer in vitro and in vivo. Int. J. Oncol., 2008. 32(2): p. 475-80.

Hui, C., Y. Bin, Y. Xiaoping, et al., Anticancer activities of an anthocyanin-rich extract from black rice against breast cancer cells in vitro and in vivo. Nutr. Cancer, 2010. 62(8): p. 1128-36.

Bhandarkar, S.S. and J.L. Arbiser, Curcumin as an inhibitor of angiogenesis. Adv. Exp. Med. Biol., 2007. 595: p. 185-95.

Nandakumar, V., T. Singh, and S.K. Katiyar, Multi-targeted prevention and therapy of cancer by proanthocyanidins. Cancer Lett., 2008. 269(2): p. 378-87.

Wang, L.S., S.S. Hecht, S.G. Carmella, et al., Anthocyanins in black raspberries prevent esophageal tumors in rats. Cancer prevention research, 2009. 2(1): p. 84-93.

Stoner, G.D., L.S. Wang, and B.C. Casto, Laboratory and clinical studies of cancer chemoprevention by antioxidants in berries. Carcinogenesis, 2008. 29(9): p. 1665-1674.

Roy, S., S. Khanna, H.M. Alessio, et al., Anti-angiogenic property of edible berries. Free Radic. Res., 2002. 36(9): p. 1023-31.

Cavell, B.E., S.S. Syed Alwi, A. Donlevy, et al., Anti-angiogenic effects of dietary isothiocyanates: mechanisms of action and implications for human health. Biochem. Pharmacol., 2011. 81(3): p. 327-36.

Kunimasa, K., T. Kobayashi, K. Kaji, et al., Antiangiogenic effects of indole-3-carbinol and 3,3'-diindolylmethane are associated with their differential regulation of ERK1/2 and Akt in tube-forming HUVEC. The Journal of nutrition, 2010. 140(1): p. 1-6.

Davis, R., K.P. Singh, R. Kurzrock, et al., Sulforaphane inhibits angiogenesis through activation of FOXO transcription factors. Oncol. Rep., 2009. 22(6): p. 1473-8.

Kumar, A., S.S. D'Souza, S. Tickoo, et al., Antiangiogenic and proapoptotic activities of allyl isothiocyanate inhibit ascites tumor growth in vivo. Integrative cancer therapies, 2009. 8(1): p. 75-87.

Seyfi, P., A. Mostafaie, K. Mansouri, et al., In vitro and in vivo anti-angiogenesis effect of shallot (Allium ascalonicum): a heat-stable and flavonoid-rich fraction of shallot extract potently inhibits angiogenesis. Toxicology in vitro : an international journal published in association with BIBRA, 2010. 24(6): p. 1655-61.

Jung, S.K., K.W. Lee, S. Byun, et al., Myricetin inhibits UVB-induced angiogenesis by regulating PI-3 kinase in vivo. Carcinogenesis, 2010. 31(5): p. 911-7.

Powolny, A. and S. Singh, Multitargeted prevention and therapy of cancer by diallyl trisulfide and related Allium vegetable-derived organosulfur compounds. Cancer Lett., 2008. 269(2): p. 305-314.

Maeda, N., Y. Kokai, S. Ohtani, et al., Anti-tumor effect of orally administered spinach glycolipid fraction on implanted cancer cells, colon-26, in mice. Lipids, 2008. 43(8): p. 741-8.

Pannellini, T., M. Iezzi, M. Liberatore, et al., A dietary tomato supplement prevents prostate cancer in TRAMP mice. Cancer prevention research, 2010. 3(10): p. 1284-91.

Lu, J., K. Zhang, S. Nam, et al., Novel angiogenesis inhibitory activity in cinnamon extract blocks VEGFR2 kinase and downstream signaling. Carcinogenesis, 2010. 31(3): p. 481-8.

Kim, E.C., J.K. Min, T.Y. Kim, et al., [6]-Gingerol, a pungent ingredient of ginger, inhibits angiogenesis in vitro and in vivo. Biochem. Biophys. Res. Commun., 2005. 335(2): p. 300-8.

Min, J.K., K.Y. Han, E.C. Kim, et al., Capsaicin inhibits in vitro and in vivo angiogenesis. Cancer Res., 2004. 64(2): p. 644-51.

Jung, Y.D. and L.M. Ellis, Inhibition of tumour invasion and angiogenesis by epigallocatechin gallate (EGCG), a major component of green tea. Int. J. Exp. Pathol., 2001. 82(6): p. 309-16.

Rodriguez, S.K., W. Guo, L. Liu, et al., Green tea catechin, epigallocatechin-3-gallate, inhibits vascular endothelial growth factor angiogenic signaling by disrupting the formation of a receptor complex. International journal of cancer. Journal international du cancer, 2006. 118(7): p. 1635-44.

Domingo, D.S., M.M. Camouse, A.H. Hsia, et al., Anti-angiogenic effects of epigallocatechin-3-gallate in human skin. International journal of clinical and experimental pathology, 2010. 3(7): p. 705-9.

Murugan, R.S., G. Vinothini, Y. Hara, et al., Black tea polyphenols target matrix metalloproteinases, RECK, proangiogenic molecules and histone deacetylase in a rat hepatocarcinogenesis model. Anticancer Res., 2009. 29(6): p. 2301-5.

Wells, S.R., M.H. Jennings, C. Rome, et al., Alpha-, gamma- and delta-tocopherols reduce inflammatory angiogenesis in human microvascular endothelial cells. The Journal of nutritional biochemistry, 2010. 21(7): p. 589-97.

Miyazawa, T., A. Shibata, K. Nakagawa, et al., Anti-angiogenic function of tocotrienol. Asia Pacific journal of clinical nutrition, 2008. 17 Suppl 1: p. 253-6.

36. Szymczak, M., M. Murray, and N. Petrovic, Modulation of angiogenesis by omega-3 polyunsaturated fatty acids is mediated by cyclooxygenases. Blood, 2008. 111(7): p. 3514-21.

Llaverias, G., C. Danilo, I. Mercier, et al., Role of cholesterol in the development and progression of breast cancer. The American journal of pathology, 2011. 178(1): p. 402-12.

Llaverias, G., C. Danilo, Y. Wang, et al., A Western-type diet accelerates tumor progression in an autochthonous mouse model of prostate cancer. The American journal of pathology, 2010. 177(6): p. 3180-91.

37. Halton TL, Willett WC, Liu S, et al., Potato and french fry consumption and risk of type 2 diabetes in women. Am J Clin Nutr 2006;83(2):284-90.

38. Pisani P. Hyper-insulinaemia and cancer, meta-analyses of epidemiological studies. Arch Physiol Biochem. 2008 Feb;114(1):63-70.

Gallagher EJ, LeRoith D. The proliferating role of insulin and insulin-like growth factors in cancer. Trends Endocrinol Metab. 2010 Oct;21(10):610-8.

Gnagnarella P, Gandini S, La Vecchia C, Maisonneuve P. Glycemic index, glycemic load, and cancer risk: a meta-analysis. Am J Clin Nutr. 2008 Jun;87(6):1793-801.

Dong JY, Qin LQ. Dietary glycemic index, glycemic load, and risk of breast cancer: meta-analysis of prospective cohort studies. Breast Cancer Res Treat. 2011 Apr;126(2):287-94.

39. Barclay AW, Petocz P, McMillan-Price J, et al. Glycemic index, glycemic load, and chronic disease risk—a meta-analysis of observational studies. Am J Clin Nutr. 2008 Mar;87(3):627-37.

40. Fasano A. Leaky gut and autoimmune diseases. Clin Rev Allergy Immunol. 2012 Feb;42(1):71-8.

41. Kjeldsen-Kragh J, Hvatum M, Haugen M, et al. Antibodies against dietary antigens in rheumatoid arthritis patents treated with fasting and a one-year vegetarian diet. Clin Exp Rheumatol 1995;13(2):167-172.

Nenonen M, Törrönen R, Häkkinen AS, et al. Antioxidants in vegan diet and rheumatic disorders. Toxicology. 2000;155(1-3):45-53.

Müller H, de Toledo FW, Resch KL, et al. Fasting followed by vegetarian diet in patients with rheumatoid arthritis: a systematic review. Scand J Rheumatol. 2001;30(1):1-10.

McDougall J, Bruce B, Spiller G, et al. Effects of a very low-fat, vegan diet in subjects with rheumatoid arthritis. J Altern Complement Med. 2002;8(1):71-75.

42. Clemmons DR, Seek MM, Underwood LE. Supplemental essential amino acids augment the somatomedin-C/insulin-like growth factor I response to refeeding after fasting. Metabolism 1985;34:391-395.

Allen NE, Appleby PN, Davey GK, et al. The associations of diet with serum insulin-like growth factor I and its main binding proteins in 292 women meat-eaters, vegetarians, and vegans. Cancer Epidemiol Biomarkers Prev 2002;11:1441-1448.

43. Werner H, Bruchim I. The insulin-like growth factor-I receptor as an oncogene. Arch Physiol Biochem 2009;115:58-71.
Kaaks R. Nutrition, insulin, IGF-1 metabolism and cancer risk: a summary of epidemiological evidence. Novartis Found Symp 2004;262:247-260; discussion 260-268.

44. Continuous Update Project Interim Report Summary. Food, Nutrition, Physical Activity, and the Prevention of Colorectal Cancer. World Cancer Research Fund / American Institute for Cancer Research.; 2011.
Wu J, Dong S, Liu G, et al. Cooking process: a new source of unintentionally produced dioxins? J Agric Food Chem 2011;59:5444-5449.

45. National High Blood Pressure Education Program, National Heart, Lung, and Blood Institute. National Institutes of Health. "National High Blood Pressure Education Program Working Group report on primary prevention of hypertension." Arch Intern Med 1993;153:186-208
Tsugane S. Salt, salted food intake, and risk of gastric cancer: epidemiologic evidence. Cancer Sci. 2005 Jan;96(1):1-6.
Frassetto LA, Morris RC Jr, Sellmeyer DE, Sebastian A. Adverse effects of sodium chloride on bone in the aging human population resulting from habitual consumption of typical American diets. J Nutr. 2008 Feb;138(2):419S-422S.

46. Simopoulos AP. The importance of the omega-6/omega-3 fatty acid ratio in cardiovascular disease and other chronic diseases. Exp Biol Med (Maywood). 2008 Jun;233(6):674-88.

47. Nieman DC, Henson DA, Austin MD, Sha W. Upper respiratory tract infection is reduced in physically fit and active adults. Br J Sports Med. 2011 Sep;45(12):987-92.

48. Ferreira MG, Valente JG, Gonçalves-Silva RM, Sichieri R. Alcohol consumption and abdominal fat in blood donors. Rev Saude Publica. 2008 Dec;42(6):1067-73. Sesso HD, Cook NR, Buring JE, et al.. Alcohol consumption and the risk of hypertension in women and men. Hypertension. 2008 Apr;51(4):1080-7.

49. Phend, C. MedPage Today. SABCS: Moderate Drinking Boosts Breast Cancer Recurrence. http://www.medpagetoday.com/MeetingCoverage/SABCS/17444
Singletary KW, Gapstur SM. Alcohol and breast cancer: review of epidemiologic and experimental evidence and potential mechanisms. JAMA. 2001 Nov7;286(17):2143-51.

50. George A, Figueredo VM. Alcohol and arrhythmias: a comprehensive review. J Cardiovasc Med (Hagerstown). 2010 Apr;11(4):221-8.

51. American Heart Association: Alcohol, Wine, and Cardiovascular Disease. http://www.americanheart.org/presenter.jhtml?identifier=4422

52. Mayne ST. Beta-carotene, carotenoids, and disease prevention in humans. FASEB J. 1996 May;10(7):690-701.

53. Melhus H, Michaëlsson K, Kindmark A, et al. Excessive dietary intake of vitamin A is associated with reduced bone mineral density and increased risk for hip fracture. Ann Intern Med. 1998 Nov 15;129(10):770-8.

54. Botto LD, Loffredo C, Scanlon KS, et al. Vitamin A and cardiac outflow tract defects. Epidemiology. 2001Sep;12(5):491-6.

55. Bjelakovic G, Nikolova D, Gluud LL, et al. Antioxidant supplements for prevention of mortality in healthy participants and patients with various diseases. Cochrane Database Syst Rev. 2008 Apr 16;(2):CD007176.

56. Brewer GJ. Iron and Copper Toxicity in Diseases of Aging, Particularly Atherosclerosis and Alzheimer's Disease. Exp Biol Med 232 (2): 323. 2007

57. Charles D, Ness AR, Campbell D, et al. Taking folate in pregnancy and risk of maternal breast cancer. BMJ. 2004 Dec 11;329(7479):1375-6.

58. Figueiredo JC, Grau MV, Haile RW, et al. Folic acid and risk of prostate cancer: results from a randomized clinical trial. J Natl Cancer Inst. 2009 Mar 18;101(6):432-5.
Fife J, Raniga S, Hider PN, Frizelle FA. Folic acid supplementation and colorectal cancer risk: a meta-analysis. Colorectal Dis. 2011 Feb;13(2):132-7.

59. Sellers TA, Kushi LH, Cerhan JR, et al. Dietary folate intake, alcohol, and risk of breast cancer in a prospective study of postmenopausal women. Epidemiology. 2001Jul;12(4):420-8.
Charles D, Ness AR, Campbell D, et al. Taking folate in pregnancy and risk of maternal breast cancer. BMJ. 2004 Dec 11;329(7479):1375-6.

60. Johnson RK, Appel LJ, Brands M, et al.; American Heart Association Nutrition Committee of the Council on Nutrition, Physical Activity, and Metabolism and the Council on Epidemiology and Prevention. Dietary sugars intake and cardiovascular health: a scientific statement from the American Heart Association. Circulation. 2009 Sep15;120(11):1011-20.

61. Joseph JA, Shukitt-Hale B, Willis LM. Grape juice, berries, and walnuts affect brain aging and behavior. J Nutr. 2009 Sep;139(9):1813S-7S.

62. Bazzano LA, Li TY, Joshipura KJ, Hu FB. Intake of fruit, vegetables, and fruit juices and risk of diabetes in women. Diabetes Care. 2008 Jul;31(7):1311-7.

63. Cao G, Shukitt-Hale B, Bickford PC, et al. Hyperoxia-induced changes in antioxidant capacity and the effect of dietary antioxidants, J Appl Physiol 1999;86(6):1817-22.

64. Jedrychowski W, Maugeri U, Popiela T, et al. Case-control study on beneficial effect of regular consumption of apples on colorectal cancer risk in a population with relatively low intake of fruits and vegetables. Eur J Cancer Prev. 2010 Jan;19(1):42-7.

65. Foschi R, Pelucchi C, Dal Maso L, et al. Citrus fruit and cancer risk in a network of case-control studies. Cancer Causes Control. 2010 Feb;21(2):237-42.

66. Block G, Paterson, B, Sabar A. Fruit,Vegetables and Cancer Prevention: a review of epidemiological evidence. Nutr Cancer 1992;18 (1):1-29. van Duijnhoven FJ, Bueno-De-Mesquita HB,

Ferrari P, et al. Fruit, vegetables, and colorectal cancer risk: the European Prospective Investigation into Cancer and Nutrition. Am J Clin Nutr. 2009 May;89(5):1441-52.

67. Maynard M, Gunnell D, Emmett P, et al. Fruit, vegetables and antioxidants in childhood and risk of cancer: the Boyd Orr cohort. J Epidimiol Community Health 2003;57:219-225.

68. Larsson SC, Orsini N, Wolk A. Milk, milk products and lactose intake and ovarian cancer risk: a meta-analysis of epidemiological studies. Int J Cancer. 2006 Jan 15;118(2):431-41. Qin LQ, Xu JY, Wang PY, et al. Milk consumption is a risk factor for prostate cancer: meta-analysis of case-control studies. Nutr Cancer. 2004;48(1):22-7.